Vera
The KING'S
Daughter

ISBN 978-1-936208-35-7

Layout and cover design: Lydia Zook
Front cover background images: istockphoto.com

Printed in the USA
Second printing: February 2013

For more information about Christian Aid Ministries, see page 197.

Published by:
TGS International
P.O. Box 355
Berlin, Ohio 44610 USA
Phone: 330·893·4828
Fax: 330·893·2305
www.tgsinternational.com

TGS000615

Vera
The KING'S
Daughter

Harvey Yoder

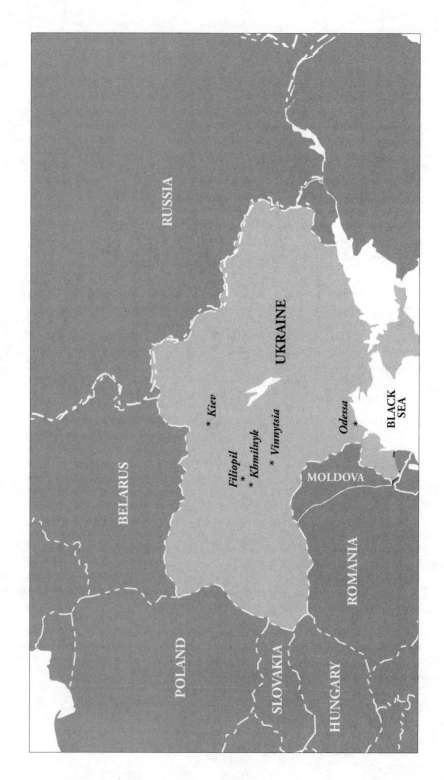

Table of Contents

Defenseless 1

The green fields of central Ukraine seemed to undulate gently as the breeze stirred the young wheat. The village of Filiopil,* with its five thousand residents, covered the top of a gently rounded hill. By 1947 the collective farms had already been established long enough to make the landscape mundanely similar over the plains of central and eastern Ukraine.

In a field south of the village and next to the farm pond, several dozen farm workers hoed the corn, weeding and thinning the rows by hand. Men and women, young and old worked in staggered rows as they labored under the early summer sun. At the edge of the field, several large oak trees created an oasis of shade on the tall grass. This was where the farm workers had left their jackets and jugs of water.

Nine-year-old Vasily sat among the jackets, his brow beetled into a permanent scowl. He dug a sharpened stick viciously into the ground and muttered under his breath. He looked once more at the workers moving off into the distance and spotted the two figures who were his parents. With an impatient sigh he turned his glare to the spot beside him where a toddler was escaping off her blanket once again.

With the cunning moves of a wild thing, Vasily rose from his place on the grass and crept up behind the little girl. Just as Vera tried to rise on

---
* See glossary on page 193.

unsteady legs to toddle off, he grabbed her arm, lifting her complete-ly off the ground in one angry move. His grimy free hand swung up, completely smothering his sister's tiny mouth and muffling her startled outcry. Vera winced as her frightened eyes focused on her brother's face. Her little legs dangled in the air and her free arm flailed futilely.

Abruptly, Vasily dropped her at his feet and began beating her merci-lessly with his stick, still covering Vera's mouth and nose with his hand. Her body twitched in spasms as the little girl fought for enough oxygen to keep her air-starved lungs from collapsing.

His rage temporarily spent, Vasily tossed the quivering form onto the blanket. He twirled his stick in dizzying circles above her head. "Now stay there!" he hissed venomously. Vera huddled on the blanket, draw-ing enormous shuddering sobs and cowering pitifully against the mea-ger protection of the old quilt.

Vasily stared at his little sister for a moment and then jabbed threat-eningly toward her with his sharpened stick. He looked at the working figures before shifting his attention back to Vera. He lowered the stick onto the child's head and pushed until Vera flinched and drew away. Relentlessly, Vasily pinned her down, increasing the pressure against the child's soft skull. For a long minute he kept on threatening his sister with his stick, glaring at the child with hatred in his eyes.

Finally the boy turned and went back to where the workers had put their jackets. With practiced fingers he felt inside each pocket and ex-plored the folds of every garment. Suddenly his sullen eyes lit up. Ah! There was something wrapped up in a piece of paper inside a woman's sweater. Something that felt like food!

It was only a piece of domestic cheese, but it disappeared instantly into Vasily's mouth. He wrapped a piece of oak bark inside the paper and returned the small package to the pocket. Vasily laughed with glee.

One-year-old children seem to forget easily, for Vera had already crawled off the blanket when Vasily remembered to check his sister's whereabouts. A scream of rage split the air, and Vera instinctively hud-dled down into the grass. Once more she was roughly snatched and thrown back onto the blanket.

"I will teach you," Vasily hissed through clenched teeth. After a quick glance to assure himself that none of the workers were close, he ran toward the village and disappeared between the houses.

Vera lay on the blanket, blinking her brown eyes and whimpering softly. Her arm ached where Vasily had jerked her repeatedly, and her tiny legs stung from the beating. She stuck one grubby finger into her mouth and sat up. She was all alone at the edge of the field, and the quietness that surrounded her was comforting. A trio of ravens croaked noisily as they flew into the tree above her and cocked their heads sideways to view the scene below.

When Vasily reappeared, he was still running, although with greater difficulty. In his arms he carried the old tin tub that their mother used for laundry. In spite of his burden, Vasily hurried toward his sister, once more checking the location of the workers in the field.

"You stay right there!" he shouted at Vera, and ran past her to the creek that meandered among the willows. Vera did not really understand the words, but she certainly understood the tone and cowered at the sudden outburst.

Vasily disappeared once more as the willow saplings swallowed up his form. He returned after several minutes, carrying the tub in front of him. Water sloshed from the rim onto his legs and bare feet. He set the tub of water on the ground in front of Vera, who sat on her blanket, staring fearfully at him.

When Vasily reached for her, Vera flinched and tried to draw away, but the boy captured her easily. With a few deft movements, he pulled the little girl's clothes off and plunged her into the tub.

Even in the summer, the creek water was cold as it ran beneath the trees that lined the stream. When Vera was thrust into the cold water, an involuntary cry escaped her little mouth. The tub was not big enough to immerse the small body completely, but Vasily shoved her down head-first even as she screamed and struggled to escape the frigid water.

Vasily lifted his sister's head for a moment, only to shove her back under the water as she tried to draw a breath. Vera's strangled cries only seemed to increase Vasily's rage. He glanced at the field workers and saw they were still a safe distance away, so he clamped his dirty hand over the little girl's mouth to silence her while he pinned her mercilessly in the tub.

The water chilled Vera's body, and her lungs ached for air. She began to shake uncontrollably. Hastily, Vasily jerked her out of the tub. He dabbed at her wet skin with the thin blanket and slipped her dress back over her head.

By now Vera's skin had turned white, and her lips were pale and blue. Her dark brown eyes were wide and staring, the pupils dilated unnaturally. Vasily wrapped the blanket around his little sister until she lay helpless on the ground, swaddled with her arms tightly bound to her sides.

She lay silent and unmoving, her big brown eyes looking anxiously at her brother's face as he sat on the ground watching her. Gradually her small body began to warm up, her eyes slid shut, and she fell into an exhausted sleep.

Vasily rose to his feet and checked the workers. They were trudging across the field toward the tree. From the other direction, two women carrying large baskets in each hand came from the village.

Before the workers reached him, Vasily unwrapped his little sister. Vera continued sleeping, her cheeks flushed. Vasily left her and headed toward the women bringing the lunch baskets.

"Stay away," the larger woman yelled, shaking her fist in his direction.

"What do we get today?" Vasily asked even as he heard his stomach growl.

There was no answer.

Vasily squatted as close to the women as he dared while they uncovered the food baskets. They placed the coarse bread and dried fish onto soiled white napkins. Slabs of raw white pork fat called *sala* were unwrapped from paper packages and placed alongside the bread. Another package held a bunch of slender garlic plants, limp but still green.

"Stop it, you pig!" the younger woman yelled at Vasily, who had waited until their backs were turned and then tried to grab a piece of bread. She grabbed his hair viciously, and tears stung his eyes as she yanked hair from his scalp. He scuttled back and glowered hatefully at her.

The field workers sank down on the grass amid grumbles and curses. Flasks appeared quickly, and men and women alike drank vodka. Only then did they savagely attack the food, the two women policing the hungry bunch.

"Has Vera been sleeping long?" Nadia asked her son as she sat beside the motionless toddler.

"All morning," Vasily lied easily, taking huge bites of bread and *sala*. He glanced anxiously at the rapidly disappearing food and grabbed for more. Nadia sighed and stretched herself on the grass beside her sleeping baby. She saw her laundry tub under the tree, but her weary brain could not be troubled to ask Vasily what he had been doing with the tub. She assumed it was probably some innocent pastime he had invented to occupy his time as he watched Vera.

Nadia's husband, Oleg, sat beside his wife. More than once he bent over, coughing and spitting onto the ground. His lined face looked old and worn.

"You rat!" one of the women hissed suddenly at Vasily. He cowered slightly under her enraged glare. The woman had rummaged in her sweater for the cheese and found only the piece of wrapped bark. Her hatred seared the air between the two and Vasily dropped his gaze for a moment. Then he glowered insolently back at her.

"Vera screams too much and won't stay where I put her." Vasily glared defiantly at his mother, who had grabbed him by the collar and was twisting his shirt until he nearly choked.

This time Nadia had caught Vasily giving Vera the cold water treatment. Severe stomach pains had rendered her useless in the fields, so she had been permitted to return home from the collective farm.

The laundry tub was still filled with water, this time from the well located on their street. As soon as Vasily had heard the yard gate bang shut, he had sprung up with the dripping wet Vera still struggling to get her breath. But his mother had seen. Ignoring the pain in her side, Nadia pounced furiously onto Vasily before he could react.

The enraged mother shook her son like a dog shakes a rat. Vera lay naked beside them on the dirty blanket, wailing in a thin, piping voice. Nadia abruptly thrust Vasily away from her and knelt beside her daughter. Gathering her up, she cradled the miserable child in her arms.

"How often have you been doing this?" Nadia demanded.

Vasily shrugged his shoulders sullenly.

"If you ever do this again, I will beat you with a stick until you can't walk!" Nadia screamed. Suddenly she doubled over in pain from her stomach cramps.

Vasily watched heartlessly as his mother moaned in pain. When she paused for breath, he said coldly, "If you beat me, I will sell that little brat to the Gypsies." Without waiting for a reply, he dashed out of the yard and ran down the street.

Nadia groaned and staggered into the house, carrying the wailing baby. She could hardly function due to her unbearable pain. Leaving Vera wrapped in the blanket, the sick woman rushed outside and spent five minutes retching in agony.

Vera was still whimpering when Nadia finally returned. Gradually the soothing effect of the warm blanket overcame her, and the little girl fell asleep, still sobbing an occasional hiccup.

Nadia lay exhausted on the rumpled bed, her weary eyes fixed on a cheap picture of Saint Nicolas, his head encircled with a halo of gold. From his staring eyes seemed to emanate an expression of melancholy boredom. It did nothing to comfort the hopeless woman. The few other religious icons in the room looked equally remote and detached from her suffering. Nadia closed her eyes to block the stares of the saints and shuddered, wondering if they knew what sacrilegious thoughts she was thinking.

Such was the world that Vera had entered—a dismal, loveless place of emptiness with little hope for the future.

Death 2

Vera skipped across the yard and entered the small barn that housed the family's cow and their eight chickens. It was dark and gloomy inside, even in broad daylight, for the trees in the orchard kept the bright sun at bay.

"Cluck, cluck," she said soothingly to the hens. They were her friends, but the big black rooster was one to watch. He seemed to delight in pecking her bare legs whenever she turned her back.

Two hens were sitting patiently in their boxes, waiting to lay their eggs. When Vera reached under them, they clucked peevishly at the disturbance.

As she gathered the seven eggs, Vera cocked her head sideways, imitating the hens. "Now which one of you is slacking in your job?" she inquired with mock severity. "We need an egg a day from each hen." Turning to the strutting rooster, she glared at him, jutting out her lower jaw. "Why don't you get busy and lay an egg for us instead of just walking around so proudly? You could help us much more that way than just crowing all day long."

Vera wrinkled up her nose and laughed at the idea of selling eggs laid by a rooster. "I would say, 'Here is the egg that the rooster laid just for you. See how it has a bump all along the top? That is from his comb.' The ladies at the market would all come rushing every Saturday to buy your special eggs, and we could get a lot of money and buy some meat every once in a while."

Her mouth watered, and she swallowed hard at the thought of actually eating meat. She knew that even if meat was available, Mama would stretch it by using only tiny bits to flavor the potatoes or the borsch. Still, there was no harm in imagining such things.

"Vera!"

As usual, her mother's voice sounded tired. But this time there was something different in her tone. Vera noted the urgency in her mother's voice and hurried toward the house.

"I have the eggs," Vera called, ducking under a low apple tree branch and carrying her cache carefully.

"Vera," her mother repeated, looking at her nine-year-old daughter, "run and tell Priest Volodya to come. Right away!" Remembering the eggs, Nadia advanced with her apron spread out. "Here, give me the eggs, and then run," she commanded.

Vera held her apron steady while her mother took the eggs and transferred them to her own apron. "Did Papa die?" she asked bluntly, looking at her mother's red eyes.

Nadia took a deep breath and said, "No, Vera. But he will soon be dead. Now run and get the priest."

Vera knew her father was dying. It had been two months since he had taken to his bed. His rasping breath and paroxysms of coughing had gradually been taken over by wheezing. Every breath was becoming a labor for the dying man.

Death was all too common in the village of Filiopil. The elderly, young babies, and sickly children all fell victim to the dreaded but expected death. Suicides among both young and old also kept the village priest busy and the cemetery active.

It had not been particularly traumatic for Vera to accept that her father was dying. She, along with her mother and brother, had accepted that fact weeks before. The family was simply waiting for the inevitable—the death of Oleg.

Now, her apron freed from the eggs, Vera ran out the yard gate and down the street toward the small Ukrainian Orthodox church house with its tin onion dome rising above the neighboring houses.

"Father!" Vera called out as she knocked at the door, breathing hard from her sprint. "Mama said you must come. Papa is dying."

But it was not the priest who opened the door. It was his wife. Her sad eyes looked out from an expressionless face. "He's not here," she said tonelessly. "I don't know where he is."

Vera shifted from one bare foot to the other. "But Papa is dying," she persisted. "Mama wants the priest to come."

"He has not come back . . ." The woman's voice trailed off as a disturbance in the street caught her attention. Looking back at the girl in front of her, she said coldly, "He's coming."

Vera turned and watched as two men, supporting a third, came through the yard gate. The two on either side were unshaven, red-faced men, shuffling with unsteady steps toward the house, but they were in much better condition than the priest who stumbled between them. He was still dressed in his black habit, the long chain with its crucifix dangling from his neck. His black, brimless hat was gone, and his hair stood up in untidy tufts. His head wobbled uselessly about as he tried to keep up with the unsteady march toward the front door.

Vera was totally forgotten as the trio approached the waiting woman. The three men cowered visibly as the priest's wife launched into a withering verbal assault, cursing in anger and frustration.

"Well, we brought him home," one of the men managed to say in self-defense.

"Yes, you brought him home in such a state that no one wants him!" The woman had lost all apathy in her sudden fury. "All night long I am at home, waiting with the children for my husband. After you spend the entire night drinking and carousing, you bring this repulsive creature back to me? You are utterly disgusting." Her attacks were uttered between vile curses on the men, on the vodka, and on her drunken husband.

As his wife's tirade gradually penetrated his befuddled brain, Volodya raised his head and tried to focus his bleary eyes on her face. "You stop talking like that!" he slurred. "I am . . ." He faltered, and then seeing his crucifix still dangling from his neck, he grabbed it with an unsteady hand and pushed it forward. "I am," he repeated, and took a breath before finishing with great effort, "the priest!" His head bobbled forward again and lolled to one side.

"The priest!" responded his wife with venomous mockery. "You are supposed to be the priest of God to the villagers, and this is what we have!"

Suddenly she remembered Vera and turned sharply to her. "Get out of here," she commanded abruptly. "Tell your mama she is better off without a priest such as this."

Vera drew back and watched as the two men disentangled themselves from the arms of the priest. Several women had come to the fence and were watching the scene, adding their shrill opinions and scorn.

Volodya seemed suddenly infused with energy. Although he had to steady himself with one hand against the door, he dismissed his cronies with a wave of a lordly hand, shut up his wife with one look, and with a defiant gesture that was remarkable in a drunken man, sent the spectators scurrying down the street. His bleary eyes fixed on Vera. "Your father . . . is dying?" he asked in slow and labored words.

Vera nodded.

Raising one hand as though bestowing a blessing, he said, "Tell your mother that I will take a little rest and then come. The dying must be ushered into the world of the dead on the prayers of the anointed."

He seemed oblivious to the irony of calling himself anointed in his present condition. He had been ordained to the order of the priesthood by a superior in the Orthodox Church. He had studied at the Ukrainian Orthodox seminary that had managed to survive the Soviet occupation. He was a representative of God, and the villagers accepted it without question. Their religion had been passed down for countless years until it had been fused into their culture.

Vera nodded and turned to run home.

"Where is the priest?" Nadia asked sharply as soon as Vera entered the house. "Isn't he coming?"

"Not right away," Vera panted. "He wasn't at home when I got there, and then when he came back, he was completely drunk," Vera explained bluntly. "He said that after he had 'a little rest,' he would come." Vera imitated the slurred speech of the inebriated man.

Nadia snorted in disgust. "I don't know if your father will still be alive after the little rest. I don't want him to die without prayers."

Vera followed her mother into the small room where her father lay unmoving on the bed. The only sign of life came from the slow rise and fall of the blanket that covered the frail form.

"What will happen if he dies before Father Volodya comes?" Vera asked inquisitively. "Will his spirit always wander about in the air?"

"You ask too many questions, girl. Why do you ask this now? All I know is that I need the priest to come and come soon." The distraught woman sighed wearily. Crossing to the far wall where an icon was hanging, she crossed herself and bowed before she turned to leave the room.

"Vera, take the pail to the chickens," Nadia said irritably as she saw her daughter's eyes following her every movement.

"Maybe I should stay so Father won't die," Vera replied softly, glancing toward the still form on the bed.

Shocked, Nadia pulled Vera into the kitchen. "Child, you must be crazy! From what corner of your addled brain did you pull that? How could your presence keep death away?"

Vera cocked her head thoughtfully and said, "I have life in my body, and that life can spread out to my papa and give him warmth."

Nadia dropped her hand as though she had been stung. "Get out!" she hissed. "You are bewitched, child! You can do no such thing. Not even the priest can do anything like that!" With a wave of her hands, she shooed Vera outside.

With sure and strong movements, Vera climbed into the cherry tree outside the house, where she could keep watch on what was happening. She felt a strange fascination with what was occurring at her house. This was the first time she was so intimately involved with approaching death.

She wondered if Vasily knew that Father was dying. At seventeen, he was absent more often than he was at home. Just what he did was a mystery, for there was not much for young people to do in the village. Vera knew that he frequently went with his friends to a larger town about ten kilometers away and usually stayed for several days at a time. When he did show up at home again, he would sleep for a long time, and he was groggy and short-tempered for days afterward.

"Hello!"

Vera peered through the branches of the cherry tree and saw the black robes of the priest outside on the street.

Before she could swing down from her perch, the gate opened and the priest walked with measured steps across the yard to the front door. Vera was amazed at the transformation of the man. His black priest's hat was fixed solidly on his head, his black robes hung in neat folds around him, and his face had a composed look. He extended his hand to accept the kiss from Vera's mother, who met him at the door and stood aside to let him enter.

Vera went inside on quiet bare feet and stood in the doorway. Without any preliminaries, the priest was already swinging the silver incense burner that hung from a long chain. He chanted phrases in an unintelligible language as he circled the bed where the dying man lay.

When Nadia pressed several coins into his hand, he dipped into a spacious pocket and produced two thin candles. Placing them into empty holders on the table beside the bed, he lit them, and the sulfurous odor blended with the heavy smell of the incense for a moment. The candles flickered and then burned steadily.

The ritual lasted for about ten minutes. At the end of that time, the priest stooped over the dying man. Taking a vial of oil from his pocket, he moistened the inside of his forefinger slightly and dabbed it on Oleg's forehead. His singsong, high-pitched voice rose into falsetto as he made the familiar sign of the cross, first on the chest of the dying man, and then on himself.

Vera's sharp eyes saw her mother slip more coins into the priest's hands before the black-robed man left their house. Something in her rebelled at the sight of their hard-earned egg money going to the priest. She knew his family was well fed, and she could not help wondering if her mother's coins would mean another night of wild drinking for the priest.

"Wouldn't Father Volodya come again if you did not pay him?" Vera asked bluntly as soon as the yard gate banged shut.

"You ask too many questions," Nadia said, nervously twisting the folds of her skirt. "Of course he wouldn't return without pay. How else can we get him to come?"

Vera thought for a moment. "If he can save Father's soul after he dies, why does he need money to do it? Can you pay me, and I will save Father's soul?"

Nadia drew her breath in sharply and held it for a long moment. "You are saying things from the devil." She raised her hand and leaned forward until her red face was level with her daughter's eyes. "You will bring a curse on this house. Go outside right now and think about something else!"

Vera dashed out the door, her mind spinning with unanswered questions. Why were there never any answers for the questions that plagued her mind? Why did her mother become so upset when she merely wanted to understand? Just what kind of power did the priest have that no one else had? It did not make sense.

The cherry tree was a good place to be out of sight but close enough to know what was going on. It was a good place for thinking, better than her narrow bed at night when the darkness closed in and haunted her with all the unasked questions in her mind.

What would happen to Father when he died? Was the burial of the dead body the end of everything?

From inside the house she could hear Aunt Luba, her father's sister, singing and chanting the dirges she had learned as a young girl. For years, Aunt Luba had been one of a handful of singers that sang the liturgies of the church on Sundays. Now she was dragging out the high-pitched notes of the slow chant in anticipation of her brother's death.

Could Aunt Luba answer her questions? Would her mourning aunt have time for questions about death? Or more importantly, questions about life? Vera longed to know, but for now she held the questions inside.

The next day Vera was sent to the priest's house again. When she came back, this time accompanied by a sober Volodya, her father had already died.

The same ritual was followed again, but this time Nadia remained kneeling on the floor, weeping and wailing loudly. As the sound reached outside the house to the neighbors, word spread rapidly that Oleg had died.

Then there were the preparations for the funeral. How the grave in the cemetery got dug, Vera did not know. She did know, however, that the people coming into their house were trying not to let the spirit of death cling to them. They crossed themselves as they entered the little house to look at the still figure of her father, all dressed up in his best suit. Then they crossed themselves again as they left.

But no one was there to answer Vera's many questions. Why were a plate of bread and a glass of wine placed on her father's chest? Why were all the candles burning in the room until the air became so close in the summer heat that it was a wonder the living did not faint from lack of air?

The funeral day came. Vera and Vasily dressed in their best clothes and stood beside their mother, who was supported by a neighbor woman. They watched wordlessly as the priest administered the final rites before the body was taken to the cemetery.

Vera's mind became blurred as she followed the procession through the street to the burial place. The priest chanted and swung his incense holder, the women wept loudly with her mother, and Vasily walked stoically beside her, distant and aloof.

A part of Vera seemed to go down into the hole with her father's body. A feeling of claustrophobia clutched at her throat as she imagined how her father must feel, shut off from all light and air.

The same smothered feeling came back night after night as the priest kept coming to the house and offering prayers for the release of her father's spirit. "If the priest doesn't pray for your father for the required eight days," her friend Larissa told her, "then your father's spirit will not rest. It will keep hovering in the air, waiting to be released."

Vera stared at Larissa. Had she finally found someone who could answer her questions? "But Mama said we have no more money to pay the priest. He told her she could pay with eggs and potatoes for now," Vera said. "Why does it take money?"

"Oh, it takes a lot of money," Larissa said knowingly. "When my grandmother died, we hardly had anything to eat for a long time. The money has to be paid, or the spirit of the dead will come back and haunt the family. You don't want that, do you?"

A stab of fear shot through Vera. She looked around quickly and shook her head. Then, remembering how her mother took a plate of food each day and placed it on top of the newly covered grave, she asked, "Who eats the food?"

Larissa bent forward and whispered, "If the priest doesn't eat it, the poor people from the village come at night and eat it. I know."

Vera knew her family had little food to spare, but they faithfully set it out in hopes that it was enough to appease the spirit of the departed.

"On the ninth day," Larissa continued, "if the priest has prayed enough, the soul of your father leaves his body. Forty days afterward, if your mother has paid the priest enough and the priest has faithfully re-membered to pray for your father's soul, he can finally fly up to heaven. Then everything is all over and fine." Larissa shared this information with the confidence of one who had experienced it all before.

"I don't believe all that," Vera said candidly. "Vasily says that all this religious stuff is something we should get rid of. He says he does not believe the priest is any different from the rest of us."

Larissa leaned forward with wide eyes. "Your brother will go to hell!" she gasped, horrified at the sacrilege.

A bolt of fear shocked Vera's heart. She didn't want to talk with Larissa any more. "I'm going home now," she said abruptly. Turning around, she began to run. She would have liked to run from all the questions, but it was not possible. That night in her bed, they continued to haunt her. Who was right? Was her father's troubled spirit floating around in the air somewhere? To defend herself against the encroaching anxiety, she shuddered and drew her knees up to her chest.

The Accident 3

The morning sunshine made a patch of light on the worn wooden floor, and Vera made sure to step around the illuminated square. Her fanciful nature often imagined bad luck would come if she stepped in the wrong spot. There were plenty of taboos in the village—such as never whistling inside a house—and her fertile mind created many more of her own.

As she skirted the patch of sunshine and approached the cot where Vasily was sleeping, Vera saw her brother's tousled head on the thin pillow. His mouth hung open, and his breathing sounded labored and heavy in spite of his youth. Vasily was fully clothed, his body sprawled carelessly on top of the cot. Vera guessed that he had been too drunk to do more than dump himself onto the bed when he had staggered home late the night before.

One shoe was still on his foot, but the other shoe was on the floor beside the cot. His befuddled brain must have ceased functioning at that point, and he had not bothered to take his other shoe off.

Vera bent over impulsively and picked up the shoe on the floor. She placed it behind a wooden box that held Vasily's clothes, trying to make it look as though it had been tossed there. Surely her brother would not remember if he had dropped his shoe or tossed it away as he dropped into bed. Vera left the small room and ran outside.

While she was carrying water from the well to the chicken coop, she heard her mother's voice inside the house. "Vasily, get up. You have to go to work or the farm overseer will be here looking for you. You can't afford to be late one more time."

It was always like this on Mondays, with Mama trying to rouse her brother and Vasily's brain finding it difficult to rejoin his body. Only after much effort on Nadia's part would Vasily finally stumble outdoors and weave his way down the street to the collective farm to join the other workers, most of whom were in a similarly pathetic condition.

"Vasily!" Nadia's voice grew sharper. "I'll give you the water treatment if you don't get up." That threat usually worked. Even though it meant drying his bed afterward, Nadia was desperate enough to drench her son to get him out of bed.

There was silence, and Vera, waiting outside with her pail of water for the hens, guessed that Vasily was finally rousing himself. She heard his sleepy mumble, followed by Nadia saying sharply, "Well, I guess it's where you put it."

More slurred words followed, and then once more her mother spoke irritably. "Vasily, did you have the shoe when you came home? Let me see the bottom of your sock. Hmm, it's clean. That shoe must be around here somewhere."

This was the moment Vera had been waiting for. She set down the water pail and strolled inside. "What are you looking for?" she asked innocently. A mischievous gleam sparkled in her eye as she watched her mother rummaging under the cot for the missing footwear.

"Shoe," Nadia replied tersely.

"Oh?" Vera retorted, arching her eyebrows. "Vasily has lost his shoe? Oh, no, shoes cannot be lost. They cost too much money."

Vasily had been sitting listlessly on the cot, but now he let his body collapse on the bed again.

"Get up!" Nadia's voice was sharp with exasperation and worry over the missing shoe. She slapped her eighteen-year-old son on the cheek.

"Ow!" Vasily roared, sitting up and rubbing his cheek angrily. "Stop that!"

"Here is the shoe, right behind the clothes box," Vera crowed triumphantly. She tossed the shoe at her brother and looked expectantly at her mother.

Nadia grabbed the shoe without comment, shoved her son's foot inside, and tied it tightly. "Now go," she commanded, pushing him out the door.

Vera's shoulders sagged as she went outside to retrieve the pail of water. In spite of her mischievous prank, no one had thanked her for "finding" the shoe. It was as though she didn't exist.

The hens were eager to have their morning drink. One by one they dipped their beaks into the watering pan and raised their heads to let the water run down their throats. The black rooster crowed threateningly, watching Vera with his beady eyes. Finally he stopped fussing long enough to join the hens in drinking, his red wattles dipping into the water every time he lowered his head.

———

The afternoon sun was hot. Vera squatted in the garden, pulling at the weeds in the carrot row and tossing them to one side. She was alone in the garden. Actually, she was the only one at home, for both her mother and brother were at work on the collective farm. School was out, and the lonely days were supposed to be spent weeding the garden and doing other menial tasks at home.

Today was no different, except the sun seemed to be shining down on her with even more intensity than usual. Summer was in full swing, and to the young girl the work seemed endless.

Vera pulled another weed, jumped up, and began swinging the weed in a circle. The damp soil still clung to the roots, and when she released the weed, the projectile sailed off into the orchard. Vera laughed to see how far that nasty weed had sailed, and wiped her hands on her skirt.

Her throat felt parched. Water. That was what she needed. Not just water from the pail in the house, but cool water from the well down the street at the crossroad. Maybe Larissa or one of her other friends would be there. It was not hard to convince herself that she really was thirsty and that she could actually get more done in the garden after the refreshment of a nice cool drink, so Vera set off, grabbing the small pail from the shelf beside the door.

The street was nearly deserted, and Larissa was not at the well. In fact, no one was there, and even though Vera made the errand last as long as she could, she finally did decide it would be in her best interests to return home. All the way home, however, she walked with mincing steps, imagining herself to be some royal princess like Catherine the Great.

Vera stumbled over a stone in the road, and the cool water splashed out of the pail. This brought an end to her play-acting. For a moment she toyed with the idea of going back to the well for more water, but she was hot and the road was boring.

Taking a cup from the shelf in the kitchen, Vera filled it to the brim with cold water. She had forced herself to wait to drink until she could climb up to her favorite spot in the cherry tree and there let the cool water slide down her parched throat.

It was pleasant to reward herself after her self-denial. The leaves rustled companionably in the gentle breeze, and the shade was cool on her flushed cheeks. Vera bent over and noisily sipped water from the tin cup. She raised her face upward and let the water slide down her throat like the chickens did. She had to be careful to not let the water all go down at once, lest she choke and splutter.

Again and again Vera drank until the cup was empty. Then she let the cup fall and giggled as it bounced from branch to branch before tumbling into the dirt. A hen, startled at hearing the cup fall and land beside her, ran clucking in alarm. The rooster stormed over to see what had alarmed one of his hens as he loudly protested the interruption of the peaceful afternoon.

"You old king!" Vera shouted at him. She spotted a dead branch above her head and climbed up to break it off and hurl it at the lordly creature. The branch was just beyond her reach, and Vera stepped unthinkingly from her perch onto a thin limb as she stretched for the dead wood.

She felt the bough give way beneath her foot and made a desperate lunge for safety, but her hands clutched empty air and she fell. Tumbling down out of the tree, she struck her back violently against a lower branch before landing in the dust, her breath knocked out of her.

The rooster sounded the alarm, and all the hens began to cackle at the commotion. Vera lay still on the ground, her lungs deflated as she gasped for breath. Pain shot through her body, but she ignored it as she battled to breathe. Finally air began flowing into her lungs again, and she drew raspy drafts of air into her mouth.

When she tried to sit up, the intensity of the pain shooting through her back instantly caused her to lose consciousness.

The rooster, still trying to maintain control of the situation, came closer and cocked his head sideways to view the still figure in the dirt. Vera did not move.

Eventually the blackness stopped swirling about her eyes. She felt something heavy pressing on her chest, making it hard to breathe. She blinked and stared through the branches of the cherry tree to the bright blue sky beyond. Her body felt as though she had been run over by heavy machinery.

Vera tried to lift her head, and as she did so, another wave of pain shot into her back. The little girl screamed as a wall of blackness washed over her. Nausea clutched her and the scream died away in a wail of despair. She could not move. She was held to the ground as firmly as though pinned under a gigantic weight.

The rooster, startled once again, began his alarm calls, and the hens cackled in response. Vera hardly heard them as pain washed over her in waves. Her legs felt numb, and moving her head even slightly to one side caused spasms of pain to shoot into her spine.

The minutes ticked by, Vera floating into merciful unconsciousness time and again. The shadows began to lengthen, and still the young girl lay immobile.

When the yard gate finally opened and Nadia came into the yard, Vera could hardly manage a weak cry for help. "Mama!"

Nadia stopped and looked toward the orchard. "Vera?" she quavered. "Where are you?" There was no answer. Nadia started toward the chicken coop, and then she saw the small form lying still on the grass. She knew instantly that something was gravely wrong. Her energetic daughter did not lie motionless anywhere for very long. Not even to play tricks.

"Vera, what are you doing?" she demanded.

"Mama, it hurts." The weak, pathetic voice hardly sounded like Vera's.

"Where?" Anxiety made Nadia's voice sharp.

"My back."

Nadia bent over to help Vera get up. With a moan the little girl lost consciousness again.

"Help!" Nadia cried out as Vera slumped against her. In desperation she picked up her daughter and carried her into the house, Vera's legs and arms dangling helplessly.

Nadia put the girl on her bed and straightened the limp limbs. She checked to make sure Vera was breathing. Then she took a blanket and wiped the beaded sweat from the girl's forehead.

"What's wrong with her?" Vasily had come into the house and came to stand by the bed beside his mother.

"I don't know," replied Nadia bleakly. "I came home and found her lying underneath the cherry tree. I tried to help her up, and she just passed out. She has not responded since I brought her in." Nadia sank wearily onto the bed beside Vera.

"Fell out of the tree, most likely," Vasily remarked casually. "You going to make something to eat?"

"Vasily, be reasonable. I have to stay here with Vera. She might be dying, and you ask for something to eat? Get your own food." Nadia voiced her fear and spoke sharply.

With a snort of disgust, Vasily left the house without bothering to look for anything. He would go somewhere else to find food, and more importantly, drink.

With a moan Vera opened her eyes weakly. Seeing her mother, she said, "Oh, Mama, it hurts so badly."

"Where?" Nadia's voice was gentle now.

"My back."

Nadia did not immediately reply. She pushed back her fears and finally said as cheerfully as she could, "You lie still and I will get you something to eat. You just rest right here. By morning you will be running around again." Something deep inside her doubted those words, but she did not know what else to say.

"No, Mama," was all Vera managed to say when her mother brought her a piece of bread. "I need water."

But there was no way the injured girl could lift her head to drink from the water glass without crying out in agony. Finally Nadia soaked a piece of cloth in the water and let it dribble into Vera's mouth.

The water felt good to her parched throat, but as soon as it entered her stomach, she became nauseous again and could swallow no more.

Tears streamed from Vera's eyes and splashed onto the blanket beneath her. The pain just kept coming in waves that offered no relief.

Nadia briefly considered taking her daughter to the hospital, but she knew that any movement would be excruciatingly painful and decided to wait until the next morning to see how things stood.

So began a long, weary night for both mother and daughter. Vera drifted off into sleep, only to wake up crying in pain. Nadia tried to alleviate the pain by any method she could think of, but nothing helped. Only after hours of pitiful crying would Vera drift off to sleep, only to wake up and begin the cycle all over again.

Nadia felt the unfairness of her life grip at her heart. Her husband was dead, her son was fast becoming an alcoholic, and now her daughter was seriously injured. What did life offer her? Nothing.

In the dim light of the morning, the distressed woman looked blankly at the wall in front of her. The icon of Saint Stephen looked back with melancholy eyes from its lofty perch.

Nadia crossed herself and tried to remember the lines of the prayers she had been taught as a girl. Her weary mind could not recall the ancient Slavic words, and she bent forward to rest her head on the bed beside Vera. Within moments she fell asleep.

Heedless of the pain and suffering inside the house, the rooster roused himself as the morning light began chasing the darkness away. With a mighty crow he announced to the world that another day was dawning.

Then he chortled contentedly and flew down from his perch, inviting the hens to follow him.

Futility 4

"Well, she will eventually burst if she can't pass her water," the neighbor lady said heartlessly. She looked casually down at Vera, who was curled in a fetal position. "How long since she last went?"

"Three days," Nadia sighed wearily.

"Then she will die," Anya said tactlessly. "You must take her to the hospital."

For about a week after her fall, Vera had been unable to do anything more than lie flat on her back. Eventually she had managed to turn onto her side and pull her legs up to her stomach to alleviate the pain somewhat. From then on she had stayed in this position, occasionally working herself from one side to the other.

Nadia had fashioned rough diapers for her daughter after repeated accidents in bed. Forced by the farm boss to go back to work after only two days at home caring for her injured daughter, Nadia attempted to push Vera's desperate situation from her mind. It was easier to cope if she didn't allow herself to dwell on the dire possibilities. Now, however, there was no escaping the fact that something was dreadfully wrong with Vera.

"How can I take her to the hospital?" the mother asked wearily.

"Get the farm wagon. I will speak with the farm boss." Anya made the decision for Nadia. "You must get this child to the doctor."

"Severe injuries to the spine." The doctor turned from the frail form on the examining table to face Nadia. "She will need to stay and have extended treatments."

Nadia's face fell and her shoulders sagged in despair. "How long?" she inquired hollowly.

The doctor shrugged. "At least six weeks to two months. Maybe longer. We will see how she responds to the treatments."

Nadia knew the hospital would provide only the bare necessities, and she would need to travel back and forth to bring food for her daughter. No one could survive on the skimpy food that was occasionally served to the patients.

"No, no," she moaned, dissolving into tears. The doctor shrugged his shoulders and left the room. Weeping women were common enough in the hospital that Nadia's tears of despair had no effect on him.

Without a word to her daughter, Nadia returned home. Vera remained curled up on the table until two nurses came and trundled her away on a wheeled stretcher. She moaned in pain at every jostle, but at least it was not as rough as the excruciating journey on the farm wagon had been. The young girl no longer cried, for there were no more tears to respond to the agonizing pain that continued to surge through her.

"She will die in there," all the neighbors clucked indignantly at Nadia, shaking their heads. "The hospitals are understaffed, and no one will care for your daughter."

"They will not release her until the doctor signs the papers," Nadia told them with eyes red from weeping. "I cannot bear to see her there by herself." She felt a twinge of conscience as she remembered that Vera had been left by herself during each day even before she had gone to the hospital.

"Get her out of that hospital," demanded Gregory, a powerfully built farm worker. "Just take her out. You are the mother." He jutted his head forward and spoke belligerently.

Nadia began to weep again. "I can't do it. They speak to me as though I am too stupid to know anything."

Gregory took another swig from his bottle. "Leave it to me," he said brashly. "I'll get her out of that hospital." So it was that the village man, emboldened by constant swigs from the bottle, entered the hospital. He bundled Vera in his overcoat and loudly proclaimed, "I am her father," as he carried her off.

"Don't ever bring her back and expect us to help," the doctor yelled after the departing man. "If you kill her, it will be on your record."

"I won't kill her any more than you will," Gregory shouted back. "We villagers know some things your knives and medicines will never know. We heal our own."

By this time everyone in the village had an interest in the invalid and an opinion about her treatment. Neighbors came daily to offer home-made remedies and advice.

"Hit her on her back with stinging nettles to bring the blood flow back and carry off the diseased parts," suggested a well-meaning neighbor. Predictably, the nettles did nothing for Vera's poor back except cause her more discomfort in the form of a rash.

When none of the crude and cruel treatments worked on the hapless girl, Vera began to spend long days alone in bed. Fortunately, her kidneys and bladder eventually began to function normally again.

The pain had gradually subsided into a constant ache that she managed to ignore for the most part. During the day, curled up in her most comfortable fetal position, Vera kept herself occupied with her thoughts. At night she would often wake up, finding herself crying in pain. Her back became bent as if she was constantly stooping.

"Her spine is growing that way because she is still so young," a chiropractor told Nadia after she had made another long and arduous journey to the city in an attempt to find healing for Vera. "She will always be a hunchback. Her legs, too, will never be straight, for she keeps her knees bent up all the time. It would be good to get her legs straightened out." He began pulling at her right leg, straining against the atrophied muscles until Vera screamed in pain.

The chiropractor shrugged his shoulders with indifferent resignation. Once more Nadia took her daughter back home to lie helpless in bed day after day.

——— ——— ——— ———

"Where is the little girl who needs healing from the good white witch?" Vera heard someone enter their home more than three months after her accident. The weather was getting cold, and the warmth from the clay stove chased the dampness from their house.

"In there," Nadia replied wearily, motioning with her head.

Vera watched apprehensively as the old woman came toward her. A grin spread across the wrinkled face. With strangely glowing eyes the woman approached her bedside, whispering incantations all the while.

Vera shrank back in fear from the claw-like hands and long, dirty fingernails that stretched toward her. They hovered over her motionless form for a brief moment. Then the hands swung into motion.

"Hah, uh, hah, uh, hah!" Unintelligible sounds tumbled from the mouth of the witch as she continued to wave her hands in the air. Vera felt something inside her recoil in distaste and fear at the strange sounds and rituals.

"She will be walking in two weeks," the visitor informed Nadia confidently, laying a grimy hand on the mother's arm. Then she cupped her other hand expectantly in front of Nadia.

"I have no more money," Nadia said glumly, drawing back. "I have spent all I had and even borrowed more trying to find a cure for my daughter."

The witch drew her eyebrows together and stared at the village woman. "You could pay if you really wanted to," she hissed menacingly. "Now your daughter will always be an invalid." With a curse on the house, she left angrily.

Nadia began to weep.

Then there was the whisperer.

"Hello!" The door opened and a voice as soft and gentle as a blanket greeted Nadia one cold evening. Vasily looked up from his supper and stared at their visitor with unconcealed distaste.

An old man, bent over and walking with the help of a cane, carefully unwrapped his scarf and opened his coat. "I have come to heal the sick girl," he said in a soft whisper.

"Get out," Vasily ordered curtly. He turned back to his interrupted meal. "You can't help her any more than the rest."

"Ha, ha, ha," the old man chuckled. Even his laughter came out as a whisper. "You will take back your words when you see what Vladimir the Healer can do."

Without invitation, the old man continued into the room where Vera lay. "Little girl," he continued in whispers, "Vladimir the Healer is here. He is healing you."

Vera sensed the same dark fear she had felt when the witch had visited her. The quiet voice and the sinuous moves of the old man's hands struck terror into her heart.

"The sickness is going away into the sky. Dark is the presence coming in, and dark is the healing, the healing, the healing," chanted the old man in a hissing whisper. "We bring you this healing, this healing." Reaching into his pocket, he drew out a shriveled leather bag and began moving it back and forth over Vera's body. All the while, he kept up a slow litany of whispers, growing in intensity.

Nadia was weeping in the doorway. Vasily got up and left, slamming the front door in disgust.

With a peculiar spring the old man suddenly catapulted himself into the air and brought his hands together sharply. The loud crack of his clap startled Vera, and she stiffened instinctively with a cry of alarm. Pain shot through her body, and once more she curled herself up in her familiar position for relief.

"Healed! Healed by Vladimir the Healer!" the old man chortled softly as he watched the form on the bed. He turned toward Nadia, his hand stretched out greedily. "Pay the healer!" he demanded.

From somewhere in her dress Nadia extracted two kopeks and put them in his hands. She looked hopelessly at Vera, still curled up miserably on the bed.

The old man glared at the meager coins in his hand and said, again in an ominous whisper, "Healing comes in direct proportion to pay."

"I have no more," Nadia said wearily, shaking her head. "I am a poor woman."

With a swift glance around the room, the old man stepped to the wall where a small icon of Mary the mother of Jesus was hanging. With a quick motion he slipped it into his pocket.

"No!" Nadia cried in alarm, but the old man swiftly fled out the door.

"Woe on us," the distraught woman cried out to herself. "If one of the icons leaves this house, we are cursed." Rocking back and forth on her heels, she finally burst out, "Let there be an end to these healers!" Then hearing her own words, she wailed, "Oh, Lord, what am I saying? No, no! We are cursed and helpless!"

Vera tried to think. Her thoughts always seemed to be jumbled into endless cycles of pain and despair. The hospital visits, the homemade remedies, and the ill-timed healers had all failed to help her in the least.

She stared at the fixed eyes of Saint Nicolas, pictured on the largest icon in the room. Was Vasily right? He openly said there is no God. The teachers of her first and second year in school had said there is no God, but her mother feared the icons and prayed to them daily.

What about the witch and the old man who whispered? What god were they serving? It seemed that they had genuine faith in some power, but in the end, all they wanted was money. Certainly they would have been happy to see Vera get up and walk, because it would have lent credibility to their claims, but they seemed to have no real concern for her dilemma.

How long was she to remain in this miserable condition? Vera thought long and hard about her future. Even to her young mind, the life ahead looked bleak and unpleasant. Why had she even survived that fall?

"The leeches will suck all the evil out so that her body can heal. You will see. I have known this to help many people." Vera, shivering at the cold air on her exposed body as she lay face down on her bed, heard the old woman's voice, but she could not see her latest self-appointed healer.

"Here, let's put one more leech over here," the voice continued. "This one can draw out the bad blood from her lower spine."

Vera lay silent and unresisting on the bed. During all the treatments, she had found a mental escape from the atrocities forced upon her. She had learned to detach herself from her body in a way that made these treatments more bearable, even though the physical pain was sometimes acute.

"No, no, this leech treatment won't cost anything," the old woman had assured Nadia. "Let me do this for you. You cannot afford having a cripple on your hands forever. This girl needs to be healed."

Vera felt every spot where the little bloodsuckers were attached to her skin. With immense effort she willed herself to hold still and not make a sound. She tried to avoid thinking how her back must look, all covered with the leeches, swelling up as they sucked out her blood.

"See how fast they work," the old lady said exultantly. "The leeches have saliva that thins the blood and keeps the clots from forming. Then," and Vera could feel the pull of her skin as one was removed, "we let it drain, like this."

"Something is draining into the jar. There is blood as well as some kind of clear liquid," Nadia said for her own benefit as much as for Vera's.

"Yes, it's carrying away the poison and bad blood from the girl's body. That is the good way. We will have your daughter up and walking before the winter is over."

Vera had no faith in the all-too-familiar promise coming from this woman. Over and over the people who came to "help" had given a time frame for her healing. At first Vera had waited for the time with a feeling of expectation, only to be devastated when her crippled body remained the same.

She was now twelve years old. For three years she had mostly lain in bed, enduring the endless days and restless nights. She had not been helped by another brief stay in the hospital, nor by any of the myriad home remedies that were foisted on her. Her back was still hunched, her legs were still bent at the knees, and she was still confined to her bed.

Each morning and evening her mother would help her with basic necessities like a trip to the outside toilet or an occasional sponge bath. These tasks were always wearisome ordeals to be endured silently by mother and daughter.

Vera's thoughts returned to the present as she felt the last of the leeches being removed. She felt faint, and even though she was lying down, she was dizzy. Her entire body felt as though she were sinking into the thin mattress, and even her bones had an odd sensation of collapsing inside her body.

"Now cover her up, and we will soon see an improvement," the old woman's voice said from a distance. "Leeches always work."

Vera felt herself drift off into a light sleep, her strength drained away with the blood the leeches had taken.

"Holy God," Aunt Luba sang, "hear us. It is in our great weakness and sin that we humbly approach your throne. In the name of Mary and the saints, hear us, we pray!"

In spite of the ancient Slavic words of the song, Vera understood the basic meaning. One thing she did know for sure: her aunty would come at least once a month to fill their house with her chanting and singing.

Two years had passed since the leeches had been applied, and still the promised healing had not come. Now fourteen, Vera's body had grown very little since her accident. Even though she could at least wrench herself from side to side on her mattress, she was still unable to leave her bed.

"It is only by your goodness that you look on us poor sinners. Mary, mother of Jesus, beseech your Son to have mercy," the melodious chant continued.

Whenever Aunt Luba came into her scope of vision, Vera idly watched the devout woman pause in front of each icon. Crossing herself, she would bow and sometimes even kneel in front of the expressionless saints.

Vera suddenly remembered a question she had occasionally pondered in her hours of forced solitude. "Aunt Luba," she interrupted her aunt's chant suddenly, "if the saints in the icons can hear your prayers, why can't they stop the flies from dirtying them?"

Her aunt whirled toward the bed, her mouth falling open in genuine horror. "You miserable sinner!" she cried. "What sacrilegious thoughts you utter! Oh, mother of Jesus, help her!"

Vera continued sharply, "I don't think much of a god who lets flies mess all over his face. It seems to me that such a god can't have much power."

This was too much for the religious woman. Swiftly she crossed the floor to the bed where Vera lay, slapped the girl on the cheek, crossed herself, and fled the house.

Vera felt the sting of the slap, but somehow she felt acquitted. At least she had gotten a reaction. Her years of inactivity had certainly not dulled her mind. She had plenty of time to observe what was happening around her, and she had begun to question many of the religious traditions that other people seemed to accept with blind faith.

"Why do you?" she persisted, looking at Saint Andrew, his golden halo firmly in place. "Why do you let the flies mess all over you? You don't have any power to keep them off, much less help me. I haven't seen you help anyone. Mama prays to you, and what happens? First Daddy died, and now Vasily ran off and got married. Mama has to take care of the house and garden and still go to work and take care of me. Seems like you or one of the other saints should help. Even Mary, the mother of Jesus, does nothing but look at us."

Now the floodgates were opened, and Vera continued to put words to her thoughts. "I think there is nothing and nobody to help. I've had the treatments from the old people, the examinations from the doctors, the treatment from the chiropractor, and the songs from Aunt Luba. None of it helped at all."

Nadia heard the murmuring and poked her head into the room. "Why did Aunt Luba rush out the door like that?" she demanded. "Who are you talking to?"

"The saints," Vera replied cryptically.

"Oh, Lord, have mercy," Nadia wailed. "You are going crazy."

Vera felt the tightness come up into her throat, so she laughed a hard, bitter laugh.

"You laugh!" Nadia burst into tears. "You should cry instead of laugh. What a life I have. A crippled daughter who is now going crazy! I do believe you are dying. You should cry! You never cry anymore. I know you are going crazy."

Vera chuckled again, but she did not cry. Instead of tears, she felt a hardness come into her heart. A weight that had nothing to do with her crippled body was settling down on her.

Die. An idea that had been niggling in the back of her brain came swimming forward and took root in her consciousness. Why should she live? What did she have to look forward to in life? Nothing. There was absolutely nothing to live for.

Just now, Vera reflected, she was thirsty and wanted a drink. She could call out to her mother and ask her to bring her a cup of water. Then what? It would mean that only a short time later she would have to ask her mother to help her go to the pail. And, if her mother was not available at the time, she would wet her bed.

Vera had learned to do with as little as possible. She tried not to eat or drink more than absolutely necessary, for she knew that only meant more uncomfortable attempts to move her uncooperative body.

She could not think of a single thing that motivated her to stay alive. Would her mother miss her? Vera doubted it. Oh, yes, she would probably cry and wail at the funeral, but Vera was quite sure that afterward Nadia would enjoy a much better life.

More than once Vera had overheard the neighbors telling Nadia what a mercy it would be if the cripple would die. They seemed to think that if Vera's body was crippled, somehow her ears were useless too.

It was alternately funny and infuriating to Vera to observe how thoughtless people were. Hardly anyone spoke to her directly. They always spoke to Nadia about her as though Vera was a piece of furniture in the room. It usually made Vera angry, but she never said anything about it. It was simply life, and she had to deal with it.

At last Vera hatched a plan, a scheme that should bring an end to this miserable existence that was called life.

VERA, THE KING'S DAUGHTER

Desperation 5

The questions in Vera's head never went away, although they had diminished somewhat by the third day of her attempt. The fear, which was sharp at first, had dulled into a vague curiosity of what might happen if her plan actually worked. Would the anticipated flight of her soul away from her body actually free her spirit? Would there finally be rest from the weariness she endured each day?

Vera did not know. But she would find out through the only way she could think of. She would find out if Father Volodya could pray her spirit into heaven after she died, or if he would consider it her soul's just punishment to wander eternally for having intentionally ended her life.

Every time a suicide occurred in the village, there was a different atmosphere during and after the funeral. Vera had felt the grim hopelessness when she was a little girl and attended the procession to the graveyard. Maybe other people would feel that way about her. Maybe they would wag their heads and say what a pity it all was. But Vera imagined they just might be glad that she had finally released her mother from the burden she carried. Apart from her mother, Vera could not think of one person who might even miss her. All her friends had stopped coming to see her, and except for the occasional book someone dropped off for her to read, she had hardly any contact with the rest of the village.

This was the third day she had not eaten. Vera had decided to simply starve herself to death and escape the miserable existence that kept her soul imprisoned in her crippled body.

It had been relatively easy so far. When Nadia had brought her food, Vera had said nothing. She stirred the food around in the bowl and mashed the potato into bits, spreading it around to make it appear that she had eaten at least a little bit. It was not that unusual for her to eat only a few bites of a meal. Why should she be hungry? There was hardly anything that called for exertion from her to burn up the calories. Besides, the less she ate, the less she had to ask for help to go to the outhouse or use the pail.

Vera was vaguely aware that a delicious kind of stupor was gradually shrouding her. Her mind no longer had to cope with the many questions, and she fell asleep more easily and slept longer. A dark sense beckoned her to slip away into the blackness and let go of life.

"She's not eating." Through the haze of her waning consciousness, Vera heard her mother's voice. Someone had come. Vaguely she remembered hearing the outside door open and feeling a wicked draft of winter air sweeping into the house. But it had not penetrated her dulled consciousness—until now.

She felt strong hands tilt her head back firmly and spoon warm tea into her mouth. Vera's reflexes kicked in and she instinctively swallowed. Again the spoon was placed in her mouth, and again she involuntarily swallowed the sweet, warm tea. Hot broth followed the tea. Suddenly Vera could not get enough as her starved body demanded more nourishment.

"That's enough," a man's voice said. "She will get sick if she has not eaten for days."

Who was this? What man had come to see them in the winter? It sounded like Uncle Pasha, her mother's brother from a distant village. What was he doing here?

"I have come to help you, Nadia," the male voice continued. It was Uncle Pasha! "There will be a cure for your invalid."

Vera opened one eye and looked weakly at her uncle. His breath smelled from the ever-pervasive vodka, and there was no hopeful response on her part. Another person's bizarre idea of what it would take to get her out of bed and walking? Why could they not mercifully let her die?

"I will help you, my sister. Tonight we will do the treatment, and tomorrow this girl will be able to walk." His voice was commanding.

"See, I brought the dry mustard with me. Nadia, you make it into a plaster. We will put it all over Vera's back."

"We tried that before," Nadia objected halfheartedly.

"No, that is only part of the cure. I will do the rest while you make the plaster."

They both left the room, and as Vera felt her mind regain its former consciousness, she feared what else her uncle was going to do. She was aware of banging doors, footsteps going in and out, and a sharply unpleasant barnyard smell permeating the small rooms.

"The horse manure will heat up, working with the mustard plaster," Uncle Pasha said loudly. "We want to get as much heat into her back as we can. The mustard plaster will work all night, and the heat from the manure will drive the plaster deeper into her back."

Apathy settled over Vera as she resigned herself to enduring yet another half-witted scheme. She wondered how much of the idea had been fueled by the vodka.

"Give me an old blanket to put on the warming shelf," Pasha instructed his sister. "Then we will smooth the manure on that. See, it is not wet, but quite dry. Too dry, actually." His eyes roved around the room until he spied a pot of borsch simmering on the clay stove.

"Just the thing," he crowed triumphantly, and he took the ladle and moistened the manure with a generous splash of borsch.

"Phew!" Nadia cried out as the moist manure began releasing even more of the pungent smell. "Are you sure this will help?"

There was no deterring Pasha. "Is that plaster ready?" he inquired eagerly. "Put it on Vera's back, and then take a thin piece of cheesecloth and wrap it tightly around her to hold the plaster in place. Then we will lay her here on the warming shelf, and by tomorrow all the stiffness will be gone and this young lady will walk!"

Vera was encased in the plaster, wrapped up in the cocoon, and placed right on top of the horrible mess on the warming shelf. Mercifully, her mother placed a folded rag under her head to keep her hair clean.

"I sure hope this works, Pasha," Nadia said doubtfully, holding her nose. "I can't even guess what it will do to Vera if it doesn't work."

Perhaps it was the stupor that Vera still felt from her self-imposed starvation effort and the subsequent nourishment from the tea and broth that made it possible for her to endure that night.

As she lay in that awful stench, Vera first felt the moist heat penetrating deep into her back. As the long night dragged on, the moisture all dried up. An itchy, burning sensation took over. It took all of Vera's concentrated willpower to keep from screaming. But she would not make a sound. Long before, the tears had dried up inside her; and even though she felt the pain acutely, she remained silent.

Stoically she reminded herself that this was what life held for her. Her mind began forming a new plan. She would have to be more crafty the next time. Somehow she would have to hide some of the food, force herself to appear more alert, and refuse to swallow if anyone tried to force-feed her. Thinking through the plan helped the miserable girl endure the long, agonizing night.

"Vera?" Her mother's voice at last penetrated the fog of agony. "How are you? Can you move your legs? Did it work?"

"Take me off," Vera said. "My back was on fire earlier, but now I can't feel anything."

"Pasha!" Nadia called frantically when she had rolled Vera over, "come help me, quickly!" Vera heard the alarm in her mother's voice. Nadia was nearly hysterical. "Pasha, come this instant!" she screeched.

When her uncle stumbled in, Nadia said, "Look, Pasha. The cheesecloth and that mess have dried onto Vera's back like glue. The mustard and that awful horse manure are stuck to her back. I can't get it off!"

No amount of self-control could keep Vera from crying out as Pasha tried to peel the crusty mess from her back.

"No!" Nadia screamed. "You are tearing the skin off her back. It has dried right into her skin. It's bleeding all over."

The two picked her up and carried her to the bed. Vera whimpered in pain as she lay on her side, the dry mess cracking open and a searing pain causing her to break out in a cold sweat.

"Now look, Pasha. You came here drunk last night, claiming that you could help Vera, and this is what we get! She couldn't even feel anything by this morning. What kind of night she must have endured, no one can imagine. I was crazy to let you do this."

"I was sure it would help. It all dried up, didn't it?" Pasha said slowly. "It might still work though."

"Get out!" Nadia said through furious tears. "You get out of this house!"

Vera was left alone, lying in bed with the caked mess still clinging to her back. The pain from the spots where they had tried to peel the layer off her back was like hot fire. Her distraught mother, unsettled by this latest disastrous idea, had simply left the house. She could not cope with the suffering she had allowed Vera to endure.

Lying in bed trying to think how she could end her life sooner, the young girl reached a new level of despair. Numbness swept over her, and she lay for hours, seeing nothing and unaware of her surroundings.

"You've been at it again," Nadia said in exasperation. "Your back is bleeding all over."

Vera said nothing.

"I'll have to tie your hands together so you can't do that," Nadia continued in resignation. "Your back will never heal if you keep scratching yourself."

Hands tied—just another form of torture, Vera thought wearily. When Nadia had finally gotten the dry, caked mess off Vera's back, the effort left them both exhausted. Nadia had used warm grease to soften the edges, and then had worked it off piece by piece. Inevitably, a great deal of skin came away with the putrid plaster. Nadia had forced herself to finish the task, in spite of her knowledge that Vera was experiencing excruciating pain. She had left some of the grease on her daughter's back to keep the skin moist and encourage it to heal.

The plaster treatment hadn't worked. Huge scabs covered Vera's seared back, and as they dried, her back itched relentlessly. Like hundreds of fire ants eating away on her skin, the itch consumed her without mercy. She simply could not keep herself from reaching around and scratching.

"I hate to do this, but I know it is the only way you will ever leave yourself alone," Nadia said as she took strips of cloth and tied Vera's hands together. "I wish Pasha were here to see the agony he has visited on you. And on me," she added bitterly.

Vera remained silent. Her suffering body had already been subjected to so many indignities that she scarcely noticed this latest one. In a dark corner of her mind, she believed that all this suffering was her fault. She thought she must be enduring punishment for some nameless misdeed—maybe just for having been born.

For three days and nights the maddening itch on her back drove Vera to distraction. She tried rubbing her back against any hard surface and wore herself out trying to get into a position where she could get some relief by pressing her back against the head of the bed. Her atrophied muscles did very little in assisting her, and Vera found herself trying endless distortions to get rid of the insane itch.

But no sound escaped her. No tears, no laments, no wails, and no crying. Her fountain of tears had completely dried up. Somehow the young teenager managed to live through those days without losing her mind.

But clarity of mind held a torture of its own. Vera thought about how she had been cheated out of the mercy of death. She had failed in the attempt at starvation. What was it that cruelly kept her chained to a useless life?

Cry From the Heart 6

"Unless we do something, her legs are going to be permanently bent," Gregory told Nadia. "They must be straightened out."

Vera cringed as apprehension trickled down her injured spine.

"We will fix that," Gregory said, his strong voice carrying clearly into Vera's bedroom. "See, I have brought the board."

Sighing noiselessly, Vera held still and waited.

The burns from the mustard-manure-borsch heat treatment had finally healed. That had been three years ago. Since then, Vera had been left relatively alone by the quasi doctors who had come into her life with torturous treatments that hadn't worked. Was it to start all over again?

Since the time he had boldly carried her out of the hospital eight years earlier, Gregory had taken an occasional interest in her. Just what motivated him to come now, Vera could not even imagine.

There was a sound of footsteps as Gregory came into view. "See here?" his voice boomed. "I have made this board for you. It is straight, and I will tie your legs to the board with rope so they will bend back out and be straight."

At least he talked to her and not just about her, although he spoke as though she was much younger than her seventeen years. People forgot that she was growing up like everyone else.

"Now we will roll you over on your back," Gregory said as he moved her none too gently into a position that suited him. Slipping the board underneath her, he took the ropes and began threading them through the holes in the wood, crossing the rope over her legs.

"Wait," said Nadia, who had been watching silently. She brought strips of fabric to pad Vera's legs so the ropes would not cut into her skin.

Vera kept her eyes averted. She felt violated to have her body shoved and pushed around at the whim of this man. As usual, however, she said nothing. Silence was her only defense.

"Now we need to tighten the ropes," Gregory said as his strong hands pulled and strained against Vera's thin legs. It took an almost superhuman effort for the strong-willed girl to keep from crying out against the injustice her crippled body was bearing.

"Every day we will tighten that rope until her legs are straight." Gregory stood up and flexed his arms. "The legs will grow straight. They have to."

Nadia saw the pain and suffering in her daughter's eyes and looked away. The weary woman shrugged her shoulders and turned to leave the room. Nothing was left inside her heart to protest or to agree with the treatments. She simply accepted it as one more effort to get Vera out of bed.

Sometimes Vera wondered if her mother was so passive about all the aborted treatments because she really did not care if they killed Vera. Was her own life so empty, and did she feel so bound by her crippled daughter that either outcome was acceptable? *Either be cured or be killed,* Vera thought wryly.

"Hmm, there is still too much space between the legs and the board." Gregory ran an experimental hand under Vera's knees. His breath reeked from the vodka with which he had fortified himself before showing up at their house.

"Weight. We need to put some weight on those legs to push them down." He left the room and went into the kitchen.

"Ah!" Vera heard Gregory's triumphant cry through the waves of pain that were beginning to sweep through her thighs and lower legs. "This will be just the thing." He staggered into the room and placed a heavy bag of wheat on top of Vera's bent-up knees, adding enormous pressure onto her crippled legs. The agony from the added weight was enough to force one small cry of pain from Vera before she silenced herself with a powerful exercise of will.

Now the ropes no longer cut into her legs, but the weight of the bag of wheat overpowered all other physical sensations as it crushed her legs against the board.

"Leave it on all day. This is Sunday, so you can stay here and watch her," Gregory decided.

"I can't go to church?" Nadia's words were more a statement than a question.

"No," Gregory said emphatically. "You must stay with her." He peered at Vera's face and noted how white the invalid was. "You must watch her so she doesn't try to push off the bag."

Mercifully, the shocked nerves began to lose all feeling after a few hours, and the pain in Vera's legs gradually subsided. However, there was no numbing of the horrible backache that threatened to push her into unconsciousness.

Biting her lower lip in pain, the girl suffered quietly. She was dimly aware of her mother coming into the room several times to check on her. Vera toyed briefly with the idea of pushing against the wheat bag, but she knew her weakening muscles could not begin to dislodge it. Nadia left the house for an extended time more than once that day. Vera was sure it was because her mother did not know how to cope with this new method of torture.

With soft, trembling sobs, Vera chose the times her mother was gone to allow her feelings to crumble into grief. Her determined stoicism was fast draining away.

"Please let me die." The words from somewhere deep inside her were not directed to anyone in particular.

The picture of Saint Nicolas seemed to grow bigger as Vera succumbed to the intensity of the pain. His gaze seemed more piercing than ever, and Vera closed her eyes to shut out the stony-faced glare from the icon.

"Are you all right?" Nadia shook Vera's shoulders, rousing her from her pain-induced stupor.

In spite of her agony, Vera felt a silent giggle rise up inside her. Wracked by pain all day, her emotions and feelings hamstrung, and her mother asked if she was all right! It was simply ludicrous.

But as usual, Vera did not give in to her feelings. "No, I'm not all right," she said with effort. "I can't feel anything in my legs."

Nadia pushed the bag of wheat off her daughter's legs and cried out in shock.

Vera's legs looked like they belonged on a corpse—white, thin, and lifeless. Nadia hurriedly untied the ropes and threw the board and ropes into the corner. She began rubbing Vera's legs, trying to restore circulation to the lifeless limbs, all the while giving vent to her hopeless feelings with deep sobs.

Vera hardly felt anything. She was relieved to have the weight gone, but her consciousness was so spent that she lay quite still, helpless and in utter despair.

"This makes no sense to me either," Vera said, looking first at the big icon of Saint Nicolas and then at the smaller one of Jesus. The red heart was the most prominent feature of the latter icon, glowing scarlet against the white of Jesus' robe.

"I don't know if I am going crazy or not, but one thing I do know, the feeling I got from Vladimir the Healer and the white witch was not a good one. The hypnotist said I was too young for his spell to work on me, and the witch could do nothing but laugh whenever she saw me." Vera cocked her head and spoke to the icons.

Her mother had been gone all day to weed sugar beets. As usual, Vera was by herself in the house. Today, however, there was something unusual. It was a strange, mystical feeling that had crept into her mind.

It was an almost physical sensation, this sudden sharp awareness of a supernatural world. Vera's arms tingled and a new feeling settled in her chest. She could not identify it, but whatever it was caused her to start talking to the icons.

"If this is going crazy, I welcome it," she said aloud. "At least I can get my thoughts around whatever is happening inside me. I have never been able to do that before."

Looking at the icons again, she spoke once more to them. "Do you have any power at all? Maybe you are pictures of something that is real, but I've never heard of anyone actually being helped by any of you. You just hang there day and night, looking sorrowful and distant, totally removed from real life. Who are you?"

Vera felt oddly comforted by expressing her feelings out loud. She could not know the source of her thoughts, but she knew they were the feelings of her heart. She explored deeper.

"Do you know about the feelings I had when that crazy old woman who couldn't even speak kept throwing her head back and laughing like a demon? Do you see the black shapes trying to get into my head? Do you care?"

Vera turned her gaze away from the icons and out the small window into the cloudless blue sky. She continued talking, but not to herself, for she sensed that Someone or something was listening. "I have no purpose in life," she stated flatly. "I just exist. I am a burden to my mother, and she is the only person in my life. All the others are just trifling things." Vera laughed at her description of the neighbors and the people in their village. "They are just things that don't really care about me or what happens. They just try to relieve my mother of her burden. I am the burden."

Images of the steady stream of would-be healers and quacks paraded through her mind, but she pushed them all away. "No more," she said firmly to the sky. "I do not need any of them. I need a reason to live."

Vera fell silent, lost in her musings. Finally one thought surfaced in her mind, and she voiced it. "I need water." The request was directed at herself. Of course, she had been thirsty countless times before and had not been able to get a drink. If Nadia forgot to put water beside her bed, Vera just endured thirst that day with the usual quiet stoicism that had become part of her life.

"Why did I say that?" Vera questioned herself with a rueful laugh. The very idea of walking to get her own water! In spite of herself, she looked back at the icon of Jesus. "If you are really powerful, help me walk and get water for myself." The words tumbled from her mouth with the raw honesty of a desperate heart. "If you are actually real, then you can do it. You can make me walk. I cannot kill myself, so I need to walk. I will know that you are real if you help me. Do you hear me?"

Her words sounded ludicrous, and Vera began to laugh. At first it came out unsteadily, but it built into a wild guffaw. "I am going crazy," she told herself. A thought struck her, and she sobered abruptly. "If you make me walk, I will serve you. I don't know how, but I will live for you."

Still there was silence. Into it she screamed, "Are you real? Do you care?" The words bounced around the room. The voice sounded unlike her own, yet Vera knew it was the cry from her truest self, deep inside her heart.

"Water, I need water!" The scream rose louder, and Vera threw back her head and laughed again. The next moment she began to cry. Surprised at all this emotion, Vera nonetheless felt relief as she allowed her feelings free reign for the first time in years. Hours later, the cry still hadn't completely faded away. It continued to echo inside her head and hover over her bed. But Vera felt calmer. She had been heard, and a seed of hope sprouted in her heart.

Glimmer of Hope 7

> "He shall deliver you into the torment of everlasting darkness,
> All who have turned their backs on the Lord.
> Not one shall escape from the terribleness and majesty of God.
> Turn from your wicked ways and repent from all your sins."

The mournful dirge drifted into every corner of the small house, and as Aunt Luba sang the words, terror crept into Vera's heart. She imagined in vivid detail the torments as the song continued, describing the state of all those who died without repentance and faith in God.

Many times she was not sure exactly what her aunt was singing, for the song was sung in the ancient Slavic language that the Ukrainian Orthodox Church used. However, interspersed in the lines of the song were enough Russian words to strike terror into the teenager's heart.

Vera could not bear to look at the icons on the walls anymore. She felt sure they were somehow condemning her with their mournful and disapproving stares. They seemed to say that if they, the saints, were barely acceptable to the lofty and distant God, how could she, a crippled and useless girl, ever come close to being good enough to gain God's approval?

Vera covered her ears. She wished the song would end. Why did her aunt insist on coming and singing the chants every month? As far as Vera could see, they had accomplished nothing for anyone. Nadia always cried a lot and bemoaned the troubles that had been visited on her, as though hoping that perhaps the saints might decide she had suffered enough and had earned a little acceptance.

Darkness and light. Vera was becoming ever more conscious of the sharp difference between the two. Darkness came in clouds, bringing heavy thoughts of death, fear, heartache, and misery. Light brought an inexplicable hope that perhaps someday things might change, that one day life would have meaning.

Ever since Vera's confrontation with the unresponsive icons, something had changed in her. She could not have given a voice to what it was, but she knew things were different.

Now she often spoke her thoughts out loud when her mother was gone. She lay looking through her favorite window at the sky when it was daylight and at the stars when it was night. Especially blessed were the nights when the moon shone its silvery light on her, and for several hours Vera would lie bathed in light and enjoy a solace she could not quite explain.

"He shall deliver you into the torment of everlasting darkness." Aunt Luba's voice rose into a crescendo as she repeated the chorus once more.

"Shut up!" Vera wasn't sure if she had said the words audibly, but she no longer cared. She was not even talking to anyone, but addressing the messengers of darkness that were besieging her brain, trying once more to take her out of the light and back into the shadows.

"Oh, I need a way to keep the blackness from coming in on me," she whispered hoarsely. "I will not go into the darkness again." Yet even as she spoke, she felt the long claws of terror grab at her heart, and the agonizing slide into the lonely and deserted place began again.

In spite of her determined will, Vera felt hot tears slide down her cheeks. She shut her eyes tightly against the shadows that seemed to glide around the corners of her bed, only to see even worse images moving toward her from behind the covers of her eyelids.

"Aayy!" The cry rang out in the house as Vera opened her eyes wide, forcing herself to remain conscious.

The singing stopped abruptly, and Aunt Luba came into the room, staring at her niece. "That was a scream from the evil one," the horrified aunt said as she instinctively crossed herself in fear.

"No! It was a scream to make him go away," Vera cried wildly. "I will not live with the fear."

With a mad scramble Aunt Luba rushed out of the house, calling on all the saints and the mother of Jesus.

Vera lay panting on the bed, her eyes wide and staring. Her breathing slowly returned to normal, and she stopped trembling. "Light," she whispered to herself. "I want light to come in and keep the darkness away."

Like a flash her words from the other day came back to her. "If you are truly real, make me walk, and I will serve you." She clearly remembered the words and to whom she had spoken them. Jesus.

Not the Jesus that hung on the wall, all spotted with fly dirt. Not the Jesus who seemed remote and distant. No, there had to be another Jesus, a living, moving person who was listening. Somehow, Vera believed there could be Someone like that.

"If you are real," Vera began again, "let me know so I can live for you."

With hope rising in her heart, Vera continued to repeat the same plea over and over during the next month. She often spoke the words out loud, feeling that somehow Jesus was listening.

During that time Nadia was dutifully applying liquid paraffin to Vera's back once a week. Even though the paraffin was hot on Vera's skin, it did not cause her to blister like the mustard plaster had. It also peeled off easily, kept pliable by Vera's body heat.

Many people besides Gregory were sure that if Vera had enough heat applied to her hunched back, it would become straight and she would walk again. Detached from her treatments as much as she could be, Vera did not rebel when her mother tried yet another remedy at the urging of the villagers.

It was when she was alone that Vera experimented with the new energy that she felt surging through her. Moving her legs, pushing herself to the edge of her bed, sitting up, swinging her legs from side to side, and forcing herself to do more than she had ever done since her fall from the cherry tree, the seventeen-year-old girl felt hope rising. Perhaps she really would be able to walk again!

She ignored the pain that still plagued her. Was pain not her constant companion, as much a part of her as her arms or her useless legs? Vera deliberately chose to ignore the pain and instead focused on the new energy that infused her daily.

"If you are real," was the constant cry from her heart, "then I want to know. Please show me."

One day it happened. Vera managed to get out of bed and support herself on her own two legs, holding on to the side of the bed. Ever so slowly, she moved her feet across the floorboards in a shuffling, sideways journey to the kitchen. By the time she reached the water bucket, Vera had to fight waves of nausea, and even feared she might collapse. But she steeled herself and inched her way back to her cot.

"I did it! I did it!" The words came out triumphantly, and a feeling of euphoria swept over her in spite of the trembling and aching muscles in her back and legs.

"You are real," Vera breathed softly, still trembling with exhaustion and excitement. Awe swept over her. There must be a God, somewhere. He had heard the cry of her heart and had sent strength into her legs to make them function again.

"It was the paraffin plasters!" Nadia said triumphantly when Vera told her mother that evening of her achievement in walking to the kitchen. "Oh, yes, the heat is finally beginning to work." Then she left the house abruptly, her usual reaction to anything emotional.

"Oh, no, it wasn't," Vera scoffed out loud. "The paraffin, the mustard plaster, the hypnotist, and all the quack doctors together could not do a miracle like this. There is Someone else who has done this. I say it was God."

She was not sure exactly why she was so convinced that God had heard the words she had spoken. After all, no one had ever told her that God actually listened to the prayers and songs of the common people. The chants and dirges they performed were usually rituals performed out of a sense of duty, not acts of worship that brought them nearer to God.

It felt so good to be outside doing something useful. Vera cleaned a potato and put it in the basket beside her. Even though she walked with a permanent stoop, she had regained enough strength to move quite freely and was now in the garden helping her mother harvest the potato crop.

"You must go to church," Nadia said, pulling the basket down the row. "You need to go and take communion from the priest. You owe thanks to God."

Vera pulled another potato off the dead stalk. "I don't remember what to do in church. How will I know the rituals? I don't remember ever taking communion. Why do we even do that?"

Nadia thumped the basket down. "Questions, my girl, will not help. You just go, and the priest will tell you all you need to know. I will give you money to light candles for the saints."

"I believe God is out here," Vera said, turning her head sideways so she could look into the blue sky above them. "I do want to know God, but I don't like going to church. I don't really believe that a drunken priest is a messenger of God."

"You ungrateful girl!" Nadia almost hissed. "God heals you, and now you talk about Him in such a disrespectful manner. I have a daughter I cannot understand. You stop that talk and go on Sunday, and maybe the priest will forgive you."

Just in time Vera managed to keep herself from asking why she needed forgiveness from a man she best remembered staggering from drunkenness. Asking her mother would accomplish nothing. Nadia always seemed to get upset by her questions and thoughts about religion.

Vera sighed and gathered more potatoes from the plants her mother had dug. Were there no answers? Why did she feel so sure that God had healed her, and yet feel so frustrated by the religion of her family and community? *I will go to church,* Vera decided. *I will seek answers there.*

The Letters 8

The priest walked slowly up the aisle, chanting in a high-pitched voice that rang throughout the room. The words all blended together into a continuous string of syllables Vera could not decipher as she stood in the back leaning against the wall for support.

Three ladies, Aunt Luba in the middle, stood to one side, responding at intervals with a chant, echoing the priest's tune and probably his words.

The smell of incense was everywhere. Vera mused idly that if any of the furniture would be taken out of the church, it would always retain the smell of incense that had been burned here for decades.

Turning her head sideways to see better, Vera watched as Father Volodya majestically approached a side table where a silver chalice stood beside an ornate dish. Bending his knees to the floor and bowing his head, the priest lifted the dish and stood, holding it high toward the ceiling. Then he set the dish down again, only to pick it up once more and move it solemnly from side to side. Finally he took the lid off and placed a wafer into his mouth.

The ladies continued to sing, their voices wafting up into the high ceiling, the notes losing themselves in the nooks and corners of the cathedral. The priest repeated the ritual to bless the wine. Then he raised the chalice and took a drink.

Backing away from the table, he turned and walked to the front of the church, where he bent and kissed the feet of Jesus on the large crucifix.

At a signal from the priest, the handful of women who made up the congregation moved forward, and the priest returned to the table and passed the wafers to the women. Each of them paused to kiss his extended hand before taking the wafer. Next he passed the chalice to each of them in turn.

No one took notice of the crippled girl lingering shyly in the back. After the Mass, the priest passed right in front of Vera when he circled the cathedral, pausing in front of each of the many icons on the walls and genuflecting while swinging his incense-laden censer on the silver chain.

"Remember, O Lord, your servants! Remember your servants of the church, O Lord," Volodya chanted.

Vera tried hard to follow the words of the chant. Ah, now he was asking God to bless the priests. Then he said something about the monks and deacons, the singers and laborers of the church. The constant repetition helped Vera understand more of the song. Vera wondered if the priest thought God could not hear it the first time.

Though she waited, Vera never heard a blessing pronounced on herself or the congregation. There was plenty about the priests and deacons, but she heard nothing about the common people.

Finally the service was over and the ladies began to move toward the door, stopping and genuflecting before moving on out silently.

Vera remembered the coins and hobbled to the small table just inside the door where a wooden box with a slot in the top waited to be filled with kopeks. Vera dropped in a coin and selected two slender candles. She moved slowly toward the front of the church with her distinctive, bent-over shuffle. Then she straightened herself as well as she could. Silently she lit her two candles with the flame of one of the many burning tapers.

She felt as though she should say something, but paused, unsure how to pray. At last she murmured an awkward but heartfelt, "Thank you," and turned to leave.

The trip home seemed much longer than she had remembered. Her mind went back to the time when she had been eight years old. She remembered how quickly she had run to the priest's house to get him to pray for her dying father. Bent almost double and able to see only a few feet ahead, Vera had to keep a sharp lookout for other people.

"Hunchback, hunchback," a group of boys yelled rudely at her as they went running past.

"Yes, I am a hunchback," Vera chuckled without ill will. "But at least I'm walking. If they only knew the years I wished I could get out and walk, even if it was an awkward hunchback walk." The cruel words had merely bounced off because of the gratitude Vera felt. She could walk! She had been released from the prison of her bed.

Vera sat at the table with her mother and Vasily during one of her brother's rare visits home. "There must be different levels of holiness, and apparently I'm not very high on the list," Vera said, sopping up the last of her soup with a piece of bread. "The priest asked God to bless the priests, the monks, the deacons, and the singers, but he never asked God to bless me."

"Vera, such words!" Nadia rebuked sharply. "And just why would he ask God to bless you?"

"I'm a human being too," Vera replied simply. "And if I am a great sinner, it seems to me that I need even more blessing than the holy people. So where do I fit on this scale of holiness? Am I at the bottom?"

"May the saints have mercy!" Nadia exclaimed, throwing up her hands and staring at Vera in genuine horror. "I have raised such a stupid girl! Why can't you just go to church and be like a stump? Don't ask all these questions. Why do you continually question everything? God might make you helpless again if you are so impertinent."

"I need to know," Vera persisted. "No one has any answers for me. Everyone thinks I am crazy just for asking. Why is it so crazy to want to understand?"

Vasily glanced at Vera. "You always did want to know everything," he stated thoughtfully. "I'll tell you what. If you really want to get answers, you need to talk to Uncle Viktor. He is the only person I ever knew who seemed close to understanding God."

Nadia snorted derisively. "That old heretic! He got all confused and started going to a strange church after he moved to Russia. I know, because when he came here to visit us over twenty years ago, he kept telling us how wrong the priest was. They threw him right out of the church, they did, with all of his dangerous beliefs."

"I remember him when I was quite young, and he was nice to me," Vasily insisted. "He gave me a kopek."

"Well, you know what those Baptists do." Nadia used the local term for anyone who had left the Orthodox Church. "You can be glad that you escaped unharmed, Vasily."

"What do they do?" Vera asked with genuine interest, leaning her aching back against the wall.

"Too evil to talk about," her mother replied tightly.

"No one can prove it is true," Vasily stated matter-of-factly. "It's probably just a bunch of gossip."

Nadia snorted indignantly. "Eating children is not a light thing, Vasily," she returned heatedly. "Nor is it mere gossip when they lure adults into the water to baptize them, and then cut off their heads while they are held underwater. I have heard of this since I was a child."

"How terrible," Vera said in shock. "These are religious people?"

Vasily rose to his feet in disgust. "Mama, those tales are deliberately spread by the priests because they don't want anyone to stop coming to the cathedral. They need to keep everyone coming so they can get enough money from the people to keep them drunk. I tell you, those hypocrites are the ones who are keeping those old tales alive." Turning to his sister, he reiterated, "If you really want to get answers to your questions, you write a letter to Uncle Viktor. He is the most holy man I know. He doesn't get drunk like the priests do around here."

"Don't talk like that," Nadia scolded. "You get drunk yourself."

Vasily sniffed as he prepared to leave. "At least I don't pretend to be holy. Tell me, how holy is it when the priest throws aside his 'holy' habit and does a lot of unholy things? Remember, I go to Khmilnyk, and I see things there that most of you villagers know nothing about. I tell you, our priest is not the least bit holy."

Like a flash, the image of Volodya staggering up the walk between his drinking buddies came to Vera's mind. No, that man did not seem to be holy. Uncle Viktor? She had never even heard of him. Why did Vasily say Uncle Viktor had answers? She would find out.

The next day Vera sat at the table, painstakingly composing the letter she hoped would bring answers to her questions.

To Uncle Viktor,

This is Nadia's daughter Vera. My brother told me if I want to have answers for the questions I have about God, I should ask you. I have tried to ask people here in our village, and everyone thinks I am going crazy. Please, can you help me?

Thank you,

Vera

Vera stared at the wooden box that had come in response to her letter. Yes, it had her name on it. Its safe arrival in Filiopil all the way from Russia seemed like a miracle. Furthermore, the box had not been tampered with. The lady in charge of the post office had sent word that something had been delivered for Vera.

She heard the yard gate open. It was Aunt Luba. "What is it?" demanded her aunt. "Did you get money?"

Vera tucked the box behind her back. "And what if I did?" she replied half-teasingly.

"Well, you know we are relatives. I always did come and sing for you when you couldn't walk." Aunt Luba could actually smile.

"I haven't looked yet, but I think it is something better than money," Vera told her inquisitive aunt.

"Gold, maybe?"

"Let's see. But I'm thinking of something even better than gold." Vera felt tingly with excitement and a sense that something good was happening to her.

"Parts of the Bible," Aunt Luba said with a sniff when the package was opened. "Why, it's just pages from a worn-out book." Clearly she felt cheated.

Vera scarcely heard her. Picking up a page carefully, she began to read. She felt a shiver of excitement as she realized that this Bible was written in the familiar Russian language instead of the ancient Slavic text.

"Listen!" Vera said excitedly, pointing to the words in Matthew 5 as she read aloud. "'And seeing the multitudes, Jesus went up into the mountain. And when He had sat down, He began to preach.' I can read about Jesus right here!" she marveled.

"You need to let the priests do the reading for you. You are untrained and ignorant. Why, you are still a cripple. How can you hope to understand the Bible?" Aunt Luba crossed herself and left.

Vera continued to read eagerly. She read chapter after chapter, searching for missing pages and trying to piece together what she was reading.

In the following weeks Vera at times almost believed that Aunt Luba had been right. There were so many things in the Bible that she did not understand. The story of Nicodemus questioning Jesus resonated deeply within her. Here was someone else who had questions. But the answers Jesus gave puzzled her as much as they had puzzled Nicodemus.

The missing parts frustrated her as she read the random pages she had been sent. Stories and parables were not completed as she came to the end of a page and found nothing to continue the thread of the story.

Over and over she read the letter her great-uncle had sent with the package.

To my niece, Vera,

I am sending portions of the Bible for you to read, and I pray that you receive this package. Read it often and ask God to make it become alive for you. In this book are the answers to life's questions, and I pray that you may become a believer.

I am praying for you,
Uncle Viktor

Someone cared about her questions! It was obvious Uncle Viktor cared by the way he assured her that he was praying for her. For her, Vera! He did not even know her, and yet he was praying for her. How astonishing all this was!

"Ask God for understanding," he had written.

"I don't understand," Vera spoke out loud. "I want to understand. God, I believe you hear me. Will you please help me?"

"Ask Uncle Viktor to come." The words came clearly into Vera's mind.

Who said that? Vera wondered. She became acutely aware of a comforting Presence, and again the message registered within her.

So she wrote the second letter.

To Uncle Viktor,
Thank you for the package. I have read all the pages, and still I do not understand. Please, can you come and talk with me? I need help.
Your niece,
Vera

Vera sat motionless on her cot in the corner, but her eyes darted around the dimly lit room. Mama had drawn the curtains against the bright summer sun outside, and the thin tapers on the table in the middle of the room flickered and gave off a feeble light. Their beeswax smell was reminiscent of Sunday services at the Orthodox Church. Five candles. Apparently that was all her mother could afford.

Vera let her eyes travel once more to the still form on the wooden platform in the corner of the living room. The profile of her dead brother was etched in shadow against the white-washed wall. As the candles flickered, the shadow of Vasily's body seemed to undulate slightly. Vera looked away hastily.

Father Volodya was still muttering and swaying his lighted censer in rhythmic motions as he circled the table. His voice was low and melodious, although it sounded rather bored. Vera tried to read his expression, but the priest had his face lowered. There was nothing on his bearded face to clue her in to his thoughts. From underneath his black robe, the tips of his shoes appeared briefly before being swallowed up again beneath his voluminous skirts.

Vera glanced once again at the icons on the wall. Nothing had changed there. Still the sad eyes stared unseeing on the scene below them. The gold halos caught the flickers of candlelight, creating an eerie illusion of movement inside the gold frames.

"Bring the food," the priest said to Nadia. As Vera's mother went obediently into the kitchen, the priest paused in front of Vasily's silent form.

A sob from the kitchen brought the startling finality of death back to Vera. Just yesterday her brother had been alive. Since he had moved away from home, the sullen man had seldom visited. Village rumor speculated that he was involved in illegal activities in the local towns and was part of a gang of village thugs. Vera had not missed her brother even once since he had moved away. Any natural affection for her only sibling had long since been forgotten in her struggle to find meaning for her own life. In their circumstances there was hardly any room for compassion or normal family bonds. Therefore the abrupt news of Vasily's death only that morning had produced almost no response in Vera.

The quiet morning had been suddenly interrupted by a group of men shouting harshly for Nadia from the street in front of her house. With a loud cry of terror, Nadia had rushed from her house, somehow sensing that disaster had struck her life once more.

Then the house had been filled with men who came stumbling over the threshold with a heavy, inert burden. Vera had been unable to see between the rough men to identify whom they were carrying, but her mother's cries made it clear enough.

"My only son! Oh, blessed Virgin, look with pity on this mother!" Nadia's loud wails filled the house. "What have you done to Vasily?" she screamed hysterically at the men. She threw herself on the floor beside the lifeless form of her son.

In the tense babble of voices that came from the nervous group of men, Vera heard enough to understand that there had been a fight between two gangs. Somehow, Vasily had been given a fatal blow during the brawl.

Relieved of their burden, the men hastily left. But Nadia continued to cry and wail, "What will become of me in my old age? I have no one left to care for me! No husband and no son! There is no one left!"

As Vera listened to her mother's words, they echoed mockingly inside her shriveled heart. She silenced the protest that wanted to cry out, "You have me! I am no one. I have no value to anyone on earth. I have been unwanted all my life."

"Write to Uncle Viktor. If anyone knows anything about how to please God, he does." Vera remembered Vasily's words as she slipped a hand under her pillow to feel the precious package of pages.

A flood of emotions swept over her. The strange stirrings that had swept through her as she read and reread the pages about Jesus somehow seemed to be connected to what was happening right here. So many times she had read about the conversations Jesus had with His disciples and the things He had taught the multitudes. But the deeper meanings always seemed to elude her.

"God, I don't understand!" The simple, oft-repeated cry came from deep in her heart once more as she reflected on the events of that morning.

Within minutes, news of Vasily's death had swept through the neighboring houses. The house erupted with chaotic noise as the neighbor women came streaming in, all wailing and crying. One of them fainted and collapsed on the living room floor.

Eventually the priest arrived, cleared out the curious crowd, and began his lengthy ritual. Now he was waiting for the plate of food that Nadia had gone to fetch.

With another prayer, the priest set the plate containing a piece of bread and a cup of wine on top of Vasily's motionless chest.

According to Orthodox tradition, the spirit of the departed person was thought to hover near the body, and the food was provided in an effort to appease that spirit. Only after forty days was the spirit allowed to depart into heaven, and it was up to the family to make sure that the spirit was fed and cared for during those weeks.

Vera shook her head skeptically, and her mind continued to swirl with questions. How could an invisible spirit eat visible food? Did anyone ever see any of the food disappear into the air as the spirit ate it? At what stage of the eating would the food suddenly become invisible? But there was hardly time for her to reflect on her questions.

Burial plans were made and the grave digger was dispatched to dig another hole in the cemetery just outside the village. It was summer and the body needed to be buried the very next morning because of the heat.

Some of the neighbors, mostly older women, came back and filled the house with their clatter. Vera slipped away unnoticed and took the cow out to the banks of the stream to graze.

"Now Vasily will never know about the pages Uncle sent," Vera said out loud. "Oh, how I wish I could know what all these pages mean." An intense longing to read the now-familiar accounts came over her, but the journey back to the house to get her pages would take too long. Besides, someone would surely ask her what she was doing.

"God, are you really up there?" Vera murmured, staring into the blue sky above her. Several cumulus clouds slowly drifted overhead. The peacefulness of the sky filled her with longing for a tranquility she had never known. Vera sighed. Would she ever find answers to the tumult of questions inside her?

―――――   ――――   ―――――   ――――

A battered farm wagon stood motionless in front of the house, a tired horse standing patiently without needing to be tied.

Vera had chosen to stay outside the house that morning. Something in her rebelled at the thought of having to stay cooped up inside with all the shadows and candles and wailing women.

The night had been bad enough. Tradition had summoned several old people to stay up all night, watching over the body. Did they expect Vasily to come back to life? Did they think someone would come and steal the silent form? Vera had no idea why someone had to stay awake all night long, unless it was to keep the candles burning.

Did candles really keep away the evil spirits? Did their fragrance somehow appease a distant and uncaring God? How could Jesus be God when He was so different from Vera's notion of God? The Man whom she read about in her pages did not match her image of a wrathful God eager to punish anyone who dared question Him.

The priest came shuffling out the door, his censer swinging back and forth at the end of a long chain. He was followed by a group of village men carrying the body on a rough wooden platform. The villagers who had gathered in the streets and doorways stood silently as Vasily's form was placed on the wagon. Everyone made the sign of the cross to ward off any evil spirit that might be lurking nearby. Several people placed bouquets of flowers beside the white face before the horse jerked into action.

Vera did not try to hobble along behind the procession that wound its way out of the village, and no one seemed to notice her absence.

Dawning Light 9

The stooped shadow of the young girl leading a sway-backed cow stretched across the newly mown hayfield as the sun sank toward the horizon. It was midsummer and the light was still strong.

Vera had learned how to walk quite well, hunchbacked though she was. During the past three years her legs had become stronger. Although she still suffered frequent pain in her back, she responded stoically to her misery. Tonight, her walk was even slower than usual. She stopped and wiped her sweating brow. Her legs trembled beneath her, fatigued with the labor of holding up a crippled body. The aged cow was glad to stop as well. Lowering her head, she stretched out an enormous pink tongue and reached for a juicy clump of grass left behind by the scythe.

"I don't know why I'm not even hungry," Vera said to herself. "The emptiness in my life is so big now that I don't even want food." After the last letter she had sent to her great-uncle, there had been no response. Three months ago she had sent that letter. Why was there no answer? Her mother had suggested that perhaps Uncle Viktor had died. After all, he was an old man by now.

But Vera would not be deterred so easily. Although no one had taught the twenty-year-old girl about fasting, she had read in her portions of the Bible some references to it, so for the past three days Vera had not eaten a bite while she hoped and prayed for an answer to her letter. Drinking only water, she had taken the cow out to graze along the roads or the creek, reading and rereading the precious papers Uncle Viktor had sent to her.

She especially loved the stories where Jesus healed people. A great longing grew inside her to meet someone like Jesus. During the past few days Vera had been reading Luke 6. She was amazed that Jesus instructed the disciples to love their enemies. That was a completely new thought to her, and for days Vera pondered this. Never had she seen that kind of love in action.

In her village there was continual bickering and fighting among the residents. Enemies were despised and people were vindictive when they felt they had been wronged. How would it be possible to love enemies? The only ones who were loved were the members of one's own family, and even that love paled in comparison to what Vera's heart longed for.

Vera thought of Vasily's death. Both she and her mother had mourned his passing, but for some reason Vera never really felt that she had loved her brother. He had so rarely even been a part of her life, and on the rare occasions when he did come home, his disinterest in their lives made him seem cold and distant. Since Vasily's death, Nadia was the only remaining immediate family member for Vera to love.

Vera often wondered if she really knew what love was, especially as she now read the many teachings Jesus gave about love. What did love in action look like?

"Come." Vera tugged at the rope, and the two began their slow trek back home. The cow, splay-footed and knock-kneed, amiably followed the bent-over girl along the footpath.

When Vera pushed open the yard gate, she went in first and held the gate for the cow to follow. Then she untied the rope, and the cow went into the barn on her own.

Turning toward the house, Vera glanced through the window to see if her mother was at home. But instead of her mother's familiar face, she was startled to see the form of an old man inside, a massive beard flowing onto his chest.

"Oh, save me!" Vera murmured and put a hand against the wall to steady herself as she closed her eyes. "Is this a devil? What has he done to my mother? Am I going crazy? My mind must be playing tricks on me because I haven't eaten."

Daring to open her eyes again, she fully expected the "vision" to have disappeared, but no, the man still sat in the chair. Vera decided to confront him. She sensed that this was somehow connected with an important bend in the road of her life. Summoning her courage, she walked inside and said hesitantly, "Good day."

"Why are you so afraid of me?" the man asked gently. He smiled at Vera and stepped closer to her. "You asked me to come, and here I am. Are you not glad to see me?"

Vera sighed weakly. "Uncle Viktor! I did not know who you were." Her trembling legs buckled beneath her, and she sank onto the cot. "I thought I was having another vision when I looked in and saw you."

Nadia entered the room, and overhearing her daughter's remark, she said, "Vera has been seeing things in visions. I told her that if she keeps on reading those papers you sent her, she will become even crazier. God knows," she crossed herself rapidly, "how much trouble the devil is giving us."

Uncle Viktor lowered his big frame into a seat. "No, the Gospel does not bring trouble," he contradicted kindly. "Vera, tell me about this vision."

Vera glanced at her mother, and then fastening her eyes on the kind face of her great-uncle, she said, "I don't know if the vision was from God or not, but it seemed important." The old man nodded his head understandingly and waited.

"In my vision, Mother and I were walking on a path through a green wheat field on the way to the church. We were holding hands, and as we got to the edge of the field, the road narrowed and went around the side of a mountain. A rock wall was on one side, and the other side dropped off into a ravine so deep that I couldn't even see the bottom.

"Mother said we could not go on, because the path narrowed so much there was hardly enough room to walk even single file. I told her to hug the rock wall, and we continued slowly, both of us shaking in fear.

"Well, in my vision we arrived at the church, and a priest was inside singing the prayers. I went up to him and told him, 'What you are doing is wrong. You are leading the people in the wrong way. You are not leading them to God, and because of that, you will go to hell.'

"I hardly knew what I was saying, but the words just flew out of my mouth. The priest got very red in the face, and he said angrily, 'When I finish my service here, I am going to get my ax to kill you.' "

Nadia moaned as she heard the words from the priest in the vision. Looking nervously at Viktor, she once more crossed herself. But Uncle Viktor did not seem particularly disturbed or even surprised. Again he nodded slightly and beckoned Vera to continue.

"I told Mother that we had to flee from the church, and we ran back to the narrow road. There were many rocks and stones in our path, but we were so scared we just scrambled over the rocks, our legs all cut up and bleeding. When we got to the wheat field, Mother fell over and began crying, 'Vera, go on. Don't let him kill you!'

"I was in front, and when I heard my mother call out to me, I turned and saw her lying on the path. 'Mother! Oh, Mother!' I yelled and turned to help her. I was crying too." Vera's voice shook as she related the story, her insides churning with anxiety.

"I heard Vera screaming in her bed and came to see what was the matter," Nadia continued the story. "At first I could not even rouse her, but she kept on calling, 'Mother, Mother!' Then, when she finally came out of her trance, she could not speak."

Vera dropped her eyes. Her hands trembled, and she gripped them tightly together.

"That's when I told her she got that vision from reading those papers. There is no reason the priest would try to kill us," Nadia declared, trembling and wiping her eyes. "Why did you bother her head with such things?"

Viktor did not answer Nadia. Instead he looked at Vera and said, "Yes, I believe God sent that vision to you. What parts of it do you understand?"

Someone understood! Relief washed over Vera in an overwhelming flood. "Oh, thank you," she said. "Thank you for saying that. I really thought I was going crazy."

Shaking his head, Viktor smiled. "Quite the opposite," he chuckled. "You are at last coming into your right mind."

"You are both crazy," Nadia insisted, exiting the room. "Evil will come on this house if you turn against the priest."

Viktor understood the woman's fear. The vast majority of the rural populace lived in fear under the absolute control of the Orthodox Church. He himself had lived with this fear for many years.

"The part I understand is that the priest is not showing us how to live like Jesus taught," Vera said simply. "I have read enough about Jesus in the papers to understand that people are not living like that."

Viktor nodded, marveling at the understanding this young girl possessed. He knew without doubt that the crippled body did not house a crippled mind. Her understanding of spiritual things might still be limited, but she certainly had an open and eager heart that would keep her searching for truth.

"I did not discover that truth until I was much older than you are," Viktor told her. "My children were already grown and had their own families when I first heard the Gospel and became a believer in Jesus Christ. My wife had died, and I was lonely. There seemed to be no reason at all for me to live.

"I had known that a group of believers lived in our village, and I knew they were different from the rest of us. I, too, was afraid of the priest in our village, for he often led movements against these believers and caused them much trouble. But they never seemed to be angry, and if I passed their houses in the evening, I could hear them singing. So when my neighbor invited me to accompany him one evening, I went. They taught me the truth from God's Word, and I became a believer."

Vera listened eagerly, feeling a kinship with her great-uncle. Her heart ached with longing to know more.

"Yes, my daughter, God is a wonderful God," Uncle Viktor continued. "He loves His people very much and does not want us to live in fear. He sent Jesus to earth to experience everything that we humans go through, including death. And He conquered death so we don't have to be afraid of even that. He wants to give us peace."

Late into the night Vera and the old man continued their conversation. Viktor welcomed Vera's questions, gently pointing her to the pages of the Gospels to see what Jesus taught. He was not an educated man, and though he could not answer all of Vera's questions, his quiet faith in what he did understand gave Vera assurance of the truth of his words. A new excitement stirred the heart of the young girl. Her questions had answers, even though she didn't know all of them yet. She felt infused with a new purpose for living and the sense of a destiny that would outlive her years on earth.

"Then sings my soul, my Saviour, God to thee, how great thou art, how great thou art!" The words of the song swept over Vera, and as the voices sang the words with meaning and fervor, thrills of excitement and awe coursed through her.

How was it possible that such singing existed? This was no mournful dirge or chant like she heard in the Orthodox Church. These people were putting their whole hearts into the songs.

Uncle Viktor, sitting beside her, was singing too. He seemed right at home here in this meeting in Khmilnyk among the group of about a hundred people. Vera felt privileged to be included in this meeting of believers.

"There is a church in Khmilnyk," Viktor had told her during their conversation the evening before. "A visiting pastor told me about it recently. I made inquiries in my hometown, you know."

That morning Vera had been up at the crack of daylight and had taken as many eggs as she could find to sell at the market. They would need money to buy bus tickets to make the fifteen-minute trip to the city. The lumbering old bus passed their village out on the highway at 7:30 in the morning, so she had no time to waste.

Vera had marveled at how quickly she sold the eggs in the early morning. With her money, she had bought a bottle of lemonade and some bread. She had stuffed it in her purse, for she wanted to have something to give to Uncle Viktor.

Now the singing continued in the believers' service. Her bag was on the floor beside her, and Vera wished she had more and better food to share with her great-uncle. But as the congregation kept on singing, she forgot about food and wished she knew this song. The words seemed to carry her right out of the fear she had felt when she first entered this room of strangers.

All too soon the singing stopped and a man got up. Everyone stood reverently as he raised his hands and began talking. Vera stood up too and then realized the man was praying. She listened closely.

Why, he was praying as though God was right in this room listening to every word! She had never imagined such a thing would be done in church. As the pastor thanked God for leading him to Jesus and then asked God to bless their day of worship together, a peaceful feeling swept over the listening girl's heart.

When the prayer ended, everyone except the pastor sat down. He opened a large black book and began reading. Vera had never seen a complete Bible in her life.

"Is the Bible really that big?" Vera whispered to Uncle Viktor. He nodded and smiled. For a moment Vera felt despair creep into her heart. How could she ever hope to understand such a big book?

When he had finished reading, the pastor began to explain what he had just read. It was marvelous, for he said many of the same things that Uncle Viktor had told her the evening before!

The service lasted four hours, but Vera felt no boredom. She enjoyed the service, but she was also aware of a battle surrounding her as she contemplated this strange new way of life that sounded too good to be true. As she wrestled with her fears, she fought a choking sensation in her throat. She tried to ignore it and focus on the hopeful words of the speaker.

After the service ended, several of the church members spoke kindly to the crippled girl. Vera wondered why they made such an effort to be friendly. Why were they interested in a hunchback whom they had never met before? She was grateful but also overwhelmed. At times she had to force back the tears that threatened to undo her emotions.

Uncle Viktor seemed to realize the turmoil she was going through and did not press her to stay long. They shared the lemonade and bread on the bus ride back to the village, but for the most part the trip was made in silence.

Late into the night Vera lay curled up in her usual position on her side, reliving her experience and recalling the words of the pastor. The melody of the songs and snatches of the words kept echoing in her mind.

"God, I think I am beginning to understand just a little bit," she murmured softly. "Oh, I want more! I want to understand how to live for you!" A feeling of peace softly enveloped her, and Vera rested as one cradled in the strong arms of Someone who cared for her.

Easter Rituals 10

"Take the Easter cake, Vera. We need the blessing of the priest on our lives. Easter is the time when we get the blessing for the year." Nadia pushed the basket of special cake-like bread they called *paskha* toward her daughter as she put on her wraps before setting out to go to church.

"Mama, you know I don't believe in that," Vera protested. "I would rather not take part in something I don't believe in."

Nadia began to wail and berate Vera. "So this is my lot in life!" she cried. "My husband and son are both dead, and my daughter is inviting the devil to take a foothold in my life. How can you fly in the face of God this way?" A torrent of tears flowed down the distraught woman's face.

Vera felt the conflicting emotions wage war in her heart. She remembered clearly that Pastor Pavel had preached about this very subject. "Jesus is the only intercessor we need," the pastor had explained. "We do not need the blessing of priests or the Orthodox Church. Jesus Himself opened the way directly to God, and it is in His name that we pray and speak to God."

Tradition ran deep in the village. At Easter, in spite of the ruling Communist Party's disapproval, everyone was still expected to go to church to have the *paskha* basket blessed. Anyone not attending was considered an infidel and could expect to hear dire predictions of doom and judgment from the priest.

"Just go this one time. I won't ask anything else from you all year." Nadia sensed that Vera was wavering and pressed her advantage. "For the sake of your mother, go get the blessing."

Vera sighed silently and nodded reluctant agreement.

The crowd inside the Orthodox Church consisted mostly of women, each carrying a basket of the *paskha* bread and decorated eggs, waiting in line for the priest to pass his hand over the basket and pronounce a blessing. Vera was pushed against the wall as the crowd of able-bodied people surged forward. Bent over and supporting herself with one hand on a windowsill, she had time to reflect on the traditions she had known since she was a child. Those traditions and beliefs were being challenged by the sermons she heard from Pastor Pavel.

"We can all come before God in the name of Jesus." The words returned clearly to Vera's mind. "We do not need to ask a priest to intercede for us. Jesus Christ is our High Priest, ushering us into the presence of God."

Why was it that the villagers felt such a great need to have a priest take care of their spiritual lives? Why was the crowd of worshipers mostly women? It seemed that the only way the men celebrated Easter was by drinking more excessively than usual.

The sonorous voice of the priest swirled above the crowd. Vera caught a glimpse of him through the line of people. She guessed that he would probably join the men as soon as the service was over. No doubt, he would be as drunk as any of them by midnight.

When the line of people finally dwindled, Vera stumbled forward with her crab-like walk and offered her basket. The manner in which the priest waved his hand over her basket looked more like a dismissal than a blessing.

Again Vera felt a certain rejection as she shuffled back into the audience to finish the service. When it was over, the people did not stay to talk with each other, but rather flocked immediately to the doors.

This is not a church, Vera reflected, feeling a deep distaste for the empty rituals. Remembering her vision, she thought bitterly, *This is the abyss I saw.*

As she made her unsteady way to the door, someone in the hurrying throng inadvertently bumped into Vera, sending her stumbling against the wall. Her basket was jostled roughly against the wall, and the *paskha* tumbled out onto the floor. The eggs were cracked and broken as Vera was thrown against the basket.

Gathering the food together, Vera felt the familiar folds of frustration sweep over her. Life was so unfair. Her mother had practically forced her to come to this service, and now she was being shoved around and smashed against the wall. The people acted like a herd of cattle as they pushed and shoved to leave.

Outside the church yard were the little children who came every year to beg and ask for food from the Easter basket. But today, even they didn't want anything from Vera's basket. The bread was dirty from landing on the floor, and the eggs were cracked from their rough jostling.

"I will not go again," Vera told her mother firmly. "There was so much shoving and pushing that I couldn't get my basket blessed for a long time. Then, as we left the church, I was knocked over. Look, the food is ruined. Even the children didn't want anything from my basket."

Nadia looked at her with disapproval, but Vera continued, "I don't think anyone benefits at all by going to that church. I don't hear how we should treat each other, how God wants us to live, or anything else practical. Just the songs and chants in an ancient language and nothing to help us in our everyday lives."

"Uncle Viktor has filled your mind with heresy. Why did that man ever come to bring his false teachings?" Nadia went into her usual tirade of doom and woe. "What will become of us? The devil will take us."

Vera felt herself grow calm. "Mama, the truth Uncle Viktor has brought to us is God's truth. It is taught in the church in Khmilnyk, and it is setting me free from fear and superstitions. The devil is not going to take me. He is being chased out of here and he does not like it. But today I make a choice. I will no longer continue to be driven by our meaningless traditions."

Just hearing herself say the words brought a boldness that gave her courage. "I believe what I have been taught in the church in Khmilnyk, that Jesus gave His life on the cross for my sins, and that He rose again so we can have a new life in Him. I do not wish to spend my life weeping and sorrowing for the sins I have committed, never allowing them to be forgiven. I believe in a new life, in being born again!"

"Daughter, you are going crazy," Nadia broke into Vera's words.

"Why do you always say that when you don't understand something?" Vera asked calmly. "If this is going crazy, then it is a good crazy. Mama, do you realize that for the first time in my life, I am beginning to understand that my life has a purpose? That purpose is to live for God. I was made to serve Him." Vera knew nothing about correct theology, but she did know that the love of Christ was beginning to move inside her.

"I am praying that Uncle Viktor moves in with us. You agreed that I could invite him, and we are now waiting for his answer. He has showed me what a Christian is. I can tell you enjoy his company, Mother. Furthermore, you know he is kind and that he is one of the few men we know who does not drink. If nothing else, that should convince you that he is a godly man."

Nadia had the grace to nod her agreement. Truly the gentle old man had amazed her in the two weeks since his arrival. Always kind, doing odd jobs around the house, and never losing his temper, Uncle Viktor had blessed the house with his presence. "Well, he might as well stay since he has no family of his own," Nadia agreed.

"No!" Vera's voice was sharper than she wanted it to be, but she was upset by her mother's demand. "I told you last year that I wouldn't go again, and I will not. I don't believe in all that jargon, and the rituals do nothing for me. Or anyone else." Vera shook her head decisively.

"Our house will be cursed," Nadia wailed. "You refuse to go, and if I go, then all will know you have left and will not carry on the traditions. The village will mock us and shame us."

Easter had come around again, and Nadia was once more trying to convince her daughter to take the traditional basket of bread and eggs to be blessed by the priest.

Much had happened in the past year. Viktor had indeed returned and made his home with the two women. He had taken Vera faithfully to Khmilnyk every Sunday. He had prayed with his great-niece, and as much as he could, had answered her many questions. The early bus ride and time spent together had given much opportunity for the two to converse. True, there were many questions Vera had that the old man could not answer, yet as they asked God for wisdom, it was amazing how clearly the answers came to the two.

"No, I am a believer in Jesus Christ and not a believer in the Orthodox Church," Vera now reiterated firmly. "I will not go."

There was a shuffling of slippered feet, and Uncle Viktor came to the doorway of the kitchen. "What is the noise of loud voices about?" he asked with a smile, cupping his hand around his right ear to understand what they were saying.

"Vera will not take the *paskha* basket to get it sanctified," Nadia spoke defensively. "She took it last year."

"And I told mother I would not do it again," Vera spoke loudly so her great-uncle could hear her. "I told her I serve Jesus now."

Viktor nodded in understanding. He had seen Vera's faith grow and blossom, and he was convinced that the love of Jesus was filling her heart. "Yes, I know you serve Jesus," he agreed. "That is good."

The two women waited to see what Viktor would say. Whose side would he take?

"We can ask God to bless the basket here," he finally said, looking at the prepared basket.

A sharp intake of breath was Nadia's reaction to his suggestion. Her mind whirled. She had never heard of anything like this.

"God can send His angels, and they can bless the *paskha* just as well here as they can in church," Viktor said simply. "We know God sees all things, hears all things, and can send the angels to do whatever He wants them to do. Why don't we ask God to bless the *paskha?*"

The prayer was simple, yet direct. Viktor did not spend time saying anything momentous or profound, and yet Vera felt the presence of God as the old man simply asked the Lord to bless the food, to bless the house they were living in, and especially to bless them with His presence.

Vera marveled at the old man's wisdom. There were times when she realized that Uncle Viktor was merely a simple village peasant, uneducated and unlearned. Yet there were times like this when he amazed her with the wisdom that allowed him to address a situation and restore order and peace in such a simple way.

"God, it is you in him," she murmured her own prayer. "Over and over I thank you that my uncle was willing to hear your voice and come to bring the Good News to my life. Help me to be like him in faith and action."

Baptized 11

Pastor Pavel looked in bewilderment at the stooped form on his front porch. He tried to rub the sleep from his eyes.

"Will you come in?" he invited. "Then please begin again and tell me what you want."

Vera entered her pastor's house as the middle-aged man stepped aside and held the door for her. "Sit down," he invited his early morning guest.

"I want to be baptized," Vera began again. "I came early before the service to ask you to baptize me. I want to apply." She did not know how someone was supposed to ask to be baptized. Even Uncle Viktor had not been able to tell her. "Just ask the pastor to baptize you, I guess," he had replied when she had asked him.

Pavel was not one to be rushed. He looked thoughtfully at the young lady on the chair in his living room and asked, "Why do you want to be baptized?"

"I read the command in the Bible, and I want to be obedient." The answer came quickly, without hesitation.

"What does baptism mean to you?" Pavel asked.

"Obedience." Again the answer came quickly, this time with an emphatic nod of Vera's head.

"We are very careful whom we baptize," Pavel tried to explain. "We interview the applicant and ask for a testimony, and we also try to hear from other people, like family members."

"You don't need to ask anyone," Vera assured him. "I know what I believe."

Pavel did not reply immediately. He remembered seeing Vera in church, trying to be as inconspicuous as possible, Sunday after Sunday. Several times he had met her, but only briefly. Now Vera's sudden early Sunday morning appearance on his doorstep surprised him.

"How did you get here so early?" Pavel knew the bus did not run at this hour of the morning.

"Walked," Vera replied tersely. She pinched her lips together in a way that forestalled any further questioning.

Pavel pictured the crippled girl hobbling the five miles from her village to get to Khmilnyk. Why, she must have been up all night!

"You must be hungry," he said gently. "What can I get for you?"

Vera shrugged her shoulders and bent forward. "Water, please."

As Pavel went to get a drink for his guest, Vera looked around the room curiously. A quick evaluation showed her it was a nice house. Apparently people in the city had a little more money than the villagers. It was not luxurious, but it had a rug on the floor, several sofas, and drapes at the windows.

Vera gratefully drank the water Pavel brought her and then waited expectantly. She had come with a simple request, and she was expecting a straightforward answer.

Pavel sat back down and rubbed his hands together thoughtfully. His wife came to see who the early morning visitor was. With a smile she crossed the room and greeted Vera affectionately.

"Welcome, Sister," Ludmilla said. "What brings you here so early?"

"I want to be baptized," Vera said rather abruptly. She realized her answer came out more sharply than she had intended, but she was on a mission and could not understand the delay.

Ludmilla lifted her eyebrows and looked at her husband.

Pavel cleared his throat a little uncomfortably. "Well, Sister," he said, "we will need to interview you like I said, and we must clear it with the church elders before we can plan for baptism."

"Then you may do it now," Vera assured him. "I can wait."

Pavel tried to explain. "First I will need to speak to our deacon and the other pastor about your request. Then we will arrange a meeting with you."

Vera straightened herself up enough to look at Pavel, and with dismay she asked, "Not today?"

Pavel shook his head. "Not today. We do not hastily enter into such a serious matter."

Vera understood the serious part. She knew baptism was not a step to be taken lightly, for she had heard numerous teachings on the commitment one made to God and the church at baptism. But the part she did not understand was the delay.

"When can I come back?" She felt put off, and her frustration showed in her voice.

Pavel wanted to be sensitive to the sincere young girl, but he had to be clear. He replied firmly, "I do not know. This is not something for you to decide. We will need to interview you and then make a decision together. You must be patient."

Vera tried not to let her bitter disappointment show too much, but her eyes betrayed her.

As she got up, Ludmilla whispered into her ear, "I will be praying for you," and pressed her hand warmly. "Wait," she continued, "I will get something for you to eat. There will be a long wait before it is time for the service to begin." Rushing to her kitchen, she thrust half a loaf of bread and some cheese into a bag and gave it to Vera as she accompanied her to the door.

Vera bravely fought back the tears that threatened to spill from her eyes. She walked down the street toward the churchyard a half block away. She would sit in the back and rest where no one could see her. Her all-night walk had left her far more tired than hungry.

Her heart sore with disappointment, Vera battled waves of discouragement. She had had no idea how difficult it would be for her to be baptized.

"Well, I know Jesus has forgiven my sins and has come to live inside me." Vera placed her hand over her heart. "I have repented of my sins, and I believe that Jesus is the Son of God."

The three elders had finally come to her house. First they talked with Viktor, and then they asked Vera to come into the living room. Their questions were searching and not unkind, yet Vera felt as though they doubted the validity of her request. It was hard for her to understand why they needed to ask all the questions.

Pavel nodded his head slightly at her answer. She did seem to understand the basic idea of salvation, but he wanted to know how she had made the decision to follow Christ. He did not remember any public confession of faith in a church service. "When did you become a believer?" he inquired.

Vera cocked her head thoughtfully. "I understood almost from the first that what you were teaching was the truth. I understood it in my heart first, and as I prayed, I understood it also on the outside."

"Did someone help you repent? Did anyone pray with you?" the deacon asked.

Vera shook her head silently.

The three looked at each other. Then Pavel said, "Thank you for your answers. You may wait outside."

Vera understood that they wanted to talk among themselves, so she got up, keenly aware of three pairs of eyes watching her clumsy movements as she left the room.

She slumped on a chair in the entryway, discouraged. *It is because I am a cripple,* she thought. *No one really wants me. Like Mother says, why would they accept a hunchback into their fellowship? I am a nobody.* Quietly the distressed girl began to cry, feeling desolate and rejected.

With a clarity that made her gasp, a voice spoke suddenly and unmistakably into her heart, "I will never leave you nor forsake you!"

A gentle sensation of peace swept into Vera's heart as the Spirit ministered to her. "I have loved you from the beginning," the quiet voice continued.

Vera's heart leaped with joy. Her dejection and her sense of being unwanted and unloved vanished as the light came into her heart once more. She wiped her eyes, lifted her hands, and began pouring out words of thanksgiving and praise to Jesus.

"We need to wait," Pavel told her when the elders met her in the entryway. "When our bishop comes, we will consult with him."

After the three men left, Vera still felt the familiar pang of rejection at times. Nevertheless, she firmly forced her mind back to God and spent extra hours praying and reading her pages of the Gospel. She did not confide in anyone what she had experienced. She sensed that these tumultuous feelings were meant to test her faith and commitment.

A second meeting took place, and the elders asked Vera a few more questions.

She did not know that the elders had asked counsel from their bishop, Matias, or that he had asked them to make sure Vera really understood the commitment she was making. He also wanted to make sure Vera knew what her commitment could cost her.

The communist government was hostile toward the unregistered churches that were still baptizing and accepting members in spite of the laws that had been passed to stamp them out. Although persecution in this region was not as severe as in some other areas, anyone under the age of thirty who was baptized could face severe consequences. Even worse, the one conducting the baptism was in danger of receiving a jail sentence. All of these factors weighed heavily on the pastors of the churches, and they did not take lightly their involvement in baptizing new converts.

"How do you know that you are a child of God?" the elderly deacon asked.

Vera smiled joyfully. "I have a deep assurance that He lives inside me, and I have such peace in my heart. Before, I was so empty. I used to wonder why I, a cripple, was even alive. I knew I was a burden to my mother, and no one really needed me. But now," Vera's voice rose in excitement as she rocked back and forth on her seat, "I have this incredible peace. I know that Jesus really, truly loves me!"

It was obvious to the questioners that something remarkable had happened and continued to develop in this hunchbacked girl. Still, one of the elders said gravely, "I want you to look seriously at this step you want to take. It could very well cost you your life someday."

"It would be worth it," Vera replied without a moment's hesitation.

In spite of her blunt answers, it was evident to the three that this girl really did have a new heart. They accepted her application and spent over an hour instructing her in the teachings of the Bible. Before they left, they prayed for her. Vera felt any remaining resentment melt away as the men prayed specifically for her spiritual walk and wished her God's rich blessings.

"Be ready whenever someone calls for you," Pavel told her before they left. "We do not know when Brother Matias will come this way, but the baptism will be in the night. You must be quiet and be prepared to follow quickly when you are called."

Vera scarcely heard what he said, but nodded eagerly. She, a hunchback, was accepted and would be baptized!

Brother Matias waded out into the slow-flowing river. In the darkness his figure seemed to shrink as the water deepened. Vera watched as an elderly man she did not recognize waded out to join the bishop. She heard a murmur of low voices, first one man asking questions, then the second one answering.

Beside her, a middle-aged woman hugged a blanket around her ample figure. Vera thought she might have seen the lady several times in church, but she was not sure.

When an elderly brother from church had knocked on her door after nine o'clock, Vera had still been awake. She had been waiting for the knock and was instantly ready to accompany him.

This was not the first night she had been waiting. For nine days after the last interview, she had waited each evening, sitting up until midnight. When she finally went to bed, she remained poised in spirit to spring up if she heard anyone outside.

She had not told her mother of her plans to be baptized. Uncle Viktor knew, but she had been instructed not to tell anyone else. "It is better that others don't know," she had been told.

Her ride in the car with a driver and the elderly man who summoned her had brought Vera to a place she had never been before. It was a surreal night for her. Four people, not counting the driver who stayed in the car, were waiting beside the river.

Brother Matias had prayed softly with them, and then he waded into the water, followed by the elderly stranger.

Now there was a splash, and Vera could dimly see one of the forms disappear under the water for a moment. Then she heard more splashing, and saw the form reappear. A few moments later the old man waded back to the shore.

The lady beside Vera took her blanket off and thrust it at Vera. "Hold it for me," she requested in a low voice, and Vera could hear her voice tremble. She understood the apprehension the lady faced. She could not think of anything to say, but she hoped the woman sensed her empathy. Vera watched intently as the dark shape approached the pastor in the water.

After a few moments of quiet conversation, the woman appeared to circle the pastor in the river. She seemed to struggle for a short time before disappearing under the water. After a moment the water stirred again, and the large form of the woman resurfaced. She waded silently to the shore and took the blanket from Vera.

Now at last it was Vera's turn—the moment she had longed for intensely. With quiet prayers of thanksgiving, the crippled girl waded into the water. About halfway in, the water level was already at her perpetually stooped shoulders.

The pastor could see her approach in the dim light, and seeing that the water was becoming too deep for Vera, he signaled her to stop and waded into the shallow water to join her.

"Sister, do you believe that Jesus Christ is the Son of God?" he asked.

Vera nodded, for she could barely find her voice. "Yes, I believe that

Jesus is the Son of God," she finally managed to whisper.

"Don't be afraid," the pastor said kindly.

Vera wanted to tell him that it was not fear but joy that was robbing her of her voice, but she said nothing.

"Do you believe that Jesus died on the cross for your sins, that He rose from the grave, and that He is now in heaven interceding for you?"

"Yes," Vera said simply, "I know without a doubt that He is."

The pastor nodded. "And are you willing to take the cross of Jesus and renounce your old life with its sins? Will you turn your back to Satan and the world, choosing to live only for Jesus?"

"Oh, yes!" Vera could hardly keep from shouting the words now. "I will live for Him the rest of my life."

The words from this crippled girl resonated deeply in the pastor's heart. He had performed many baptisms, mostly at night under cover of darkness like this, but he was moved to his very soul.

"Oh, Sister, the faith that is in you will be greatly rewarded," he said. "God bless you as you receive this water baptism." And he gently lowered Vera under the water.

With streams of water flowing off her head, Vera gasped when she was raised from her baptism. Waves of emotion swept through her.

In that quiet, still night, scarcely a handful of humans witnessed what had occurred in the river. But for Vera, the sound of heavenly singing rang in her spiritual ears as she waded back to the shore, assisted by the kindly pastor. She wanted to shout and sing. Her heart was dancing, and she was acutely aware of the Holy Spirit inside her heart, enveloping her with His love and presence.

She spent the night at the home of the other lady who had been baptized and discovered that indeed there were people living in poverty greater than her own. Only a thin blanket covered the hard wooden platform that served as a bed.

"My blanket is wet from the water," the lady told her guest. "That bed is the only one I have." She nodded toward the platform. "You can have it. You look like you need it more than I do."

Vera had brought dry clothes along and had changed into them.

"Why were you going around the pastor in circles when you were in the river?" she couldn't help but ask.

"I thought I was going to drown," the woman replied. "I didn't know he was going to put me under the water until I saw what he did to that elderly man. So after the pastor asked me the questions, I asked if I had to go under the water. When he said that I did, I panicked. I grabbed at him because I was so afraid."

Vera realized that her new friend was a very simple woman with limited intelligence. "I am so glad that you wanted to be baptized for your faith in Jesus," Vera told her sincerely.

"I had heard that the Baptists sometimes cut off the heads of people when they are under the water," the woman volunteered. "I asked that man, and he said it is not true."

Vera nodded silently. That was far from the only rumor that had been circulated for years. It was also said that Christians killed and ate their own children. The malicious stories were meant to strike fear into the hearts of the Orthodox Church members and cause them to shun and even persecute any who accepted this "new and strange" faith.

Vera lay on the hard boards and drew the thin blanket up around her. At last all was quiet, and she could go into the quiet place of her heart where she had communion with her Saviour.

"Thank you," she whispered into the night. "Oh, Jesus, thank you for loving me, crippled as I am, and for taking me as your daughter. I love you with all my heart."

She felt something tickle her bent legs, but ignored it. "I really, really want to live for you the rest of my life," Vera prayed. "Teach me, Lord, how to live for you and only you. Thank you for hearing the cry of my heart when I was still only an ignorant girl and had no one to teach me about you. Thank you for Uncle Viktor and for the people at church who showed me kindness. Thank you for Brother Pavel and for Brother Matias. Bless their efforts in teaching people to find you."

The tickle on her leg turned into prickles. Something very small was inching its way up her calf. Vera reached down to scratch her leg. Then she felt something on her other leg and then something on her back.

Lice.

"Oh, Lord," Vera almost laughed aloud. "I don't think I shall be able to sleep all night. I am so blessed by you and so excited from my baptism, and now this woman's little pets are here to tickle and prickle me. I think I shall just get up and sit in a chair and talk to you all night."

The chair was hard and the position quite uncomfortable, but for the exhilarated girl, the night sped by quickly as God came and ministered joy to her heart.

A Mother's Heart 12

"The Baptists have killed her," Nadia wailed as she watched out the window for Vera's return. "With Vera, it would be easy. They would just need to have someone in the water with a knife in hand. Vera would come, trusting the man in the water, and as soon as they put her under, slash, and the head is off. I tell you, my aunt's sister said she knows of a young woman who was killed that way."

Suddenly she realized that the nearly deaf Viktor could not hear what she was saying, so she walked up to him and yelled into his face. "This is all your fault! You came here, bringing that new teaching with you, and now look where it got us! Vera believed you, and now she is gone!"

Viktor slowly shook his head and said, "Oh, Nadia. You don't even know what you are saying. Why are you so upset?"

"Upset? Would you not be angry if your daughter was missing? Last night she left. Now it's already Sunday afternoon and she still isn't here. Listen to the cow bawling because she has not been milked. We have the cow only one more day, and then she goes to Oleg's aunt for their turn to keep her." Nadia instinctively crossed herself as she said her dead husband's name. "Vera always milks the cow. I can't since I have the arthritis in my joints. Oh, I don't know what will become of us."

Rounding on the hapless man in her house, she fumed, "You just sit there, too old to be any help. You! You are the one who brought this all on us." Then, lowering her voice to keep him from hearing, she muttered, "It's high time you leave."

"Mama!"

Nadia turned toward the window. "Vera?" she breathed with a gasp.

"Yes, Mama, I'm home. I had to wait a long time for the bus today. Why, Mama, what is wrong?"

Nadia had burst into tears. Trying to hide her agitation, she fled into the garden.

Vera stood stock still, and a slow smile spread across her face. Mama had been concerned for her! That meant her mother really did love her. All the time she was milking the cow, Vera basked in the warm feeling of love. First God had showed her how much He loved her. Now she understood that her mother loved her too, when all the time Vera had felt she was simply a burden to her.

"It's because of you, God, that I understand," Vera said aloud, her head planted firmly against the flank of the cow. The long, steady streams of milk made the usual rhythmic music as her pail filled.

"If you had not taught me how to love, I think I would have missed the revelation that Mama actually loves me. All this time I was only hearing her complaining and outbursts, but I see she used this to cover up her real feelings."

A wave of love and compassion for her mother swept over Vera. She knew Nadia's life had always been bleak and dreary. With both her husband and her son gone, she had had to work hard to keep them in food and clothes. Even now, at barely fifty years old, Nadia looked old and often complained of ill health.

"God, come into Mama's heart and give her a reason to live, like you did for me." Vera poured out her petition as she finished milking. "Give me your wisdom to know how to convince her of your great love."

"He needs to go. We are poor, and he is not good for anything. He needs to go back to Russia," Nadia said decisively, yanking at a stubborn weed.

"Mama, you can't send poor Uncle Viktor away," Vera remonstrated, defending her great-uncle. "His legs are all puffy and swollen, and there is no way he could even travel home. I'll take care of him so you won't be burdened."

"You? Why, you are so little and crippled, you couldn't even help him when he needs to get up."

Vera smiled. "Oh, but you are mistaken," she told her mother. "I already have helped him many times. When you are working, I am the only one here to help him, and God gives me the strength to lift Uncle Viktor out of bed and help him walk to the outhouse."

Nadia snorted in disdain and shrugged. "Well, he is not registered here, and that is the end of that. You know the village authorities won't let this be his permanent home if he is not on the registration for this house."

"You could change that," Vera said quietly. "You could go to the village office and request his registration."

"Not for that old man who has brought such a strange belief into my home and changed you." Nadia was decisive.

"Mother, can't you see that the change in me is a good thing?" Vera asked simply. "Remember all those years when I was lying in bed with nothing to do day after day? You know I became bitter about life and tried to die. Life was bleak and empty. Now I have something to live for. I love Jesus, and He cheers me when the pain returns and I wonder what good I am on earth. He has given me a purpose to live for! I feel so different!"

Nadia looked away from Vera's shining eyes. Reluctantly she admitted, "Yes, I can see that something real has happened to you."

"It can happen to you too," Vera said eagerly. "It is not me, but Jesus in me who makes the difference. Oh, Mama, I so wish you would become a believer in Jesus Christ."

"It's okay for cripples. And old men, I suppose. I will not leave our church though—I would be punished." Nadia hastily crossed herself, trying to ward off any evil that might harm her for even talking about leaving the traditional church.

"Uncle, we must fast and pray for Mama's soul," Vera told Uncle Viktor when the two were alone in the house. She spoke loudly, for Viktor was rapidly losing his hearing.

"That woman, she is so hardened," Viktor replied testily. "She has never wanted me here, and I know that even now she is trying to get rid of me."

Vera sighed. At first Uncle Viktor had been in agreement with Vera as they prayed for Nadia, but as his mental faculties began to fade, he seemed to allow resentment to grow toward the woman who was making him feel unwelcome.

"Lord Jesus, help us," Vera prayed out loud. She felt frustrated. Her longing to see her mother become a believer only intensified. She desperately wanted someone to join her in prayer for her mother's soul. Uncle Viktor seemed to be the most obvious ally, but now his reluctance was thwarting her hopes.

"Uncle Viktor!" Vera tried again. "If we don't pray and witness, I feel that Mama's blood will be on our hands!" Tears slipped down her cheeks.

Viktor fixed his rheumy eyes on Vera. Something seemed to touch him and he mellowed.

"Please, pray and fast with me," Vera begged. "I know that if we fast, God will hear our prayers. I remember hearing in church that fasting is like breaking up the big stones in someone's mind and allowing God to enter the person's consciousness. That's what I want. I want Mama's fears to be all broken up and to disappear."

Uncle Viktor nodded. "Yes, you are right, my dear." His mind had cleared. "I will fast and pray with you."

"All this fuss and it is not even a holy day," Nadia grumbled, stirring the soup. "For three days neither of you has eaten. At least you will eat of this soup tonight."

Vera was sitting next to Uncle Viktor in the warm kitchen. Outside, the winter wind howled in the dark, spitting snow against the tiny window.

"Speak to her," Vera mouthed at Uncle Viktor after nudging him. "Tell her about Jesus."

She was so grateful that Uncle Viktor's mind had remained alert and lucid all during the fast. It was as though God had given him a reprieve from his declining health.

"Nadia," he now began, speaking very clearly, "I wonder why it is that you don't kneel and pray with your daughter. For both of us, it is not easy to kneel. I am old and Vera is crippled, yet we gladly kneel, for we love God and want to thank Him for His kindness to us. Would you not like to kneel with us?"

There was no immediate answer. Nadia briskly stirred the soup and then sighed as she turned to face the two figures on the bench. "I don't know how to pray like you do. I hear you pray, but I cannot do that. I am suspicious when I hear prayers that are not uttered by the proper authorities."

Vera heard her mother's words clearly, but Uncle Viktor cupped his hand around his ear. "What's she saying?" he inquired.

"She said she doesn't know how to pray," Vera shouted into his ear. Uncle Viktor nodded. "Will you pray with us after we eat?" he asked Nadia. "Ask God to show you if it is right for His children to pray such prayers."

The soup was hot and nourishing, but the three people eating were mostly silent, lost in their own thoughts. Vera was hungry after her fast, yet her mind was not on the soup and bread. In her heart she kept praying desperately for her mother. It was obvious that something was happening in Nadia's heart. More than once Vera saw her mother wipe her eyes and turn away from the table. She hardly touched her soup.

"I just don't know how to pray," she said again when the three knelt in the main room of the house where Nadia and Vera slept.

"Mama, you can say anything that is in your heart, and God will hear you," Vera told her. "You don't need to say any special words." She wanted to add, "You don't have to chant like the priests," but something told her not to say that. "You can just talk to Him, and He will understand."

Uncle Viktor was praying out loud, asking God to make it clear to Nadia what it meant to repent and believe.

Vera also continued to pray, but her mother said nothing.

"Did you pray?" Uncle Viktor asked Nadia after Vera helped the frail man up from his knees and onto the sofa.

"No," Nadia shook her head helplessly. "I don't know what to say."

"Do you want us to go to the kitchen so you can pray by yourself?" Uncle Viktor suggested. "Maybe you can pray better when you're alone."

Tears began falling down Nadia's wrinkled cheeks.

Vera stepped across the room and laid her hand lovingly on her mother's arm. "Sometimes all you need to say is, 'Jesus, be merciful to me, a sinner,' and He understands. He will even help you know what to pray."

"Shall we go to the kitchen, Vera?" Uncle Viktor asked, struggling to his feet.

Vera sensed that her mother still needed someone with her. "I do want to pray," Nadia was saying as she wiped her eyes. "I want to do the right thing. I want to know God."

Uncle Viktor did not understand, and again he urged, "Vera, come. Let's leave her alone."

"No, Uncle, Mama wants someone to pray with her," she said, and she knelt beside her mother.

At first Nadia could only manage, "O holy Father," over and over again, but as the Spirit began speaking to her, she found words for what was going on inside. As she cried out for forgiveness, Vera went with her every step of the way, interceding and rejoicing to see her mother's heart open toward God.

Uncle Viktor rapidly became more disoriented, and before long he lay down and fell asleep as the two women continued their prayers.

Nadia was too shy to talk about what she had experienced that evening, but Vera noticed a difference in her mother immediately. Her formerly sad eyes looked peaceful, and a quiet glow of joy shone from her face.

———

"You are now registered in this house," Nadia said several weeks later, sliding a document across the table to Uncle Viktor.

It was one of his more lucid moments, and Uncle Viktor lifted amazed eyes to the lady of the house. "Now I know that you are a believer," he said joyfully. "You got me registered so I can live in this house, and only a short time ago you tried to throw me out. You have changed!"

"You brought more into this home than just yourself," Nadia said with a hesitant smile. "You brought the presence of God with you."

Vera was overwhelmed with joy. That night she prayed, "God, this is such a wonderful miracle. I have a nearly deaf uncle whose mind is slipping, and I felt so alone. But now you gave my mother an understanding of who you are. Thank you so much, God, for doing this! How I love you for all you do!"

A great change came into their home. True, Nadia did not become a mature Christian overnight, but Vera rejoiced to see how the Lord kept on ministering to them all as they grew together in the knowledge of God.

Manna 13

The cow was gone. Even though she had been aged and nearly worn out, it had been refreshing to have her for their allotted month. Now that she was dead, the household suffered from not only the lack of dairy products to sell, but also the loss of milk to supplement their meager diet.

The chickens laid a few eggs, but since there was no grain to feed the hens during the winter, those eggs were treasured and sold for a little bit of cash. Potatoes were carefully rationed to last through the entire year until the next harvest.

These situations were not unusual for Vera, Nadia, and Uncle Viktor. Even in the best of times, getting adequate food was a struggle. And now, this fall, their food situation looked even bleaker.

"Give us this day our daily bread," was not just a rote prayer, but a heartfelt daily petition for the three. They had learned to make a small amount of food go a long way. "Yet," Vera told the other two one day, "Jesus said that we are not to worry. Just last Sunday, I remember hearing, 'Consider the lilies of the field . . . they toil not, neither do they spin . . . if God so clothe the grass of the field . . . shall he not much more clothe you, O ye of little faith?' I want to have that kind of faith."

"This has been a hard part of faith for me," Nadia said slowly. "I trust in God and pray, yet there are so many times I worry about how we can survive this winter."

Uncle Viktor said nothing, for he did not understand the conversation. Unconcernedly, he kept on eating.

Nadia watched as her relative dipped into the potato dish again. She pressed her lips together and got up. At the worktable she lifted the sieve she had used to mash the potatoes.

"Vera, do you think you could take this sieve down to the stream and wash it?" she asked. "The two cooking pots would benefit from a good soaking as well."

Vera nodded. "I will go right away. It will feel good to be in the sun for awhile. Soon enough we will have cloudy weather for months."

The periodic trip to the stream on the other side of their garden saved a long walk to the village well. The abundant water also meant that one trip to the stream allowed them to do as much washing as three trips to the well.

Vera basked in the warmth of the sun on her hunched back as she carried the utensils through the garden. Carefully she crept sideways down the small bank to where the water moved slowly through the reeds.

The soil had washed away at a curve in the stream, and small trees grew out of the bank. Vera held on to the saplings and eased her way closer to the water. Difficult as it was for her, she had done this many times. She couldn't help thinking about how easy it was for everyone else to get down the small bank, but she had learned not to dwell on her handicap or pity herself. "I am loved by God," she often reminded herself, keeping alive the joy of her salvation.

Suddenly Vera's foot slipped and she fell. The cooking pots clanked as they rolled down the bank and lay beside the water. Somehow Vera managed to hold onto the sieve, and as she righted herself, she laughed. "Now, wouldn't it have been difficult if those pots had fallen into the water? I would have had to fish them out with a stick. Thank you, Jesus. You know my limitations and you look after me."

Still smiling her gratitude, she dipped both pots into the water and set them on the bank to soak. Taking the sieve, Vera dipped it into a pool of water right next to the bank where the current had worn a deeper spot. Swishing it back and forth several times, she lifted it out and was startled to see a fish thrashing about in the bottom!

"Well, well!" Vera chuckled in surprise. The fish flopped wildly about, and Vera quickly retreated from the water, clutching her prize. She certainly did not intend to lose this delicacy.

The body of the fish looked common enough, but there was something different about its fins. As the light shone through them, they glowed red.

Curious, Vera held her hand over the thrashing fish. It was as long as her hand. Not a large fish, but it would make a very tasty addition to their soup. Carefully she scooped a hole in the soft, sandy bank. Then she pulled some dead grass and lined the hole. She placed the fish in the hole until she had finished cleaning the pots and the sieve.

Taking a handful of sand, Vera scrubbed the pots and rinsed them until they were clean. Her mouth watered at the thought of how delicious that fish would be. "God, I thank you for that fish. I know that once you sent money in the mouth of a fish, but this time you sent a fish to feed us. You do care for your children."

It was an easy thing for Vera to talk conversationally to God. Since she spent a lot of time by herself, she had found comfort in voicing her thoughts aloud. Prayer was becoming as natural as breathing for her.

"There, that's done," she said, setting the pots aside and reaching for the submerged sieve. "Maybe the current has cleaned the screen by itself, and I won't even need to scrub it."

She lifted the sieve from the water, and to her amazement, she saw another thrashing flash in the bottom. A second fish!

Although this one was not as big as the first fish, it was still big enough to eat. "How amazing," Vera marveled. "It was so easy, as though the fish were sent there just for me." Vera dumped it into the hole with its companion before dipping the sieve once more into the pool. Almost immediately she felt movement below the surface and raised the sieve to the bank. A third fish lay flopping from side to side.

Staring at the fish in disbelief, Vera felt tingles of excitement rush from her hands and into her heart.

"God!" The word was uttered in awe. "You have done this to care for us."

Only that morning they had talked about how the Lord cared for His people. They had prayed and asked God for their daily bread. "We should have asked for fish!" Vera chuckled. "This is heavenly fish!" She rinsed the sieve in the water and swung it in the air to dry it. "This is a moment to remember," she said softly. "I have received a gift straight from my Father."

Vera had experienced the deeply moving presence of the Spirit more than once in her Christian walk over the past five years, but never before in just this way. At first it happened to her when she was in church, often during the singing. She felt as though she was carried away by the beauty of the words, and she knew she was in the presence of God as she worshipped in song.

Sometimes it would happen when she was quietly meditating and reading the treasured pages that Uncle Viktor had sent to her years before. At other times it would happen when she was praying out loud, and God's presence would overwhelm her with joy. Now it had happened out here, and she knew that the fish were a gift from God.

"I have lived in this village all my life, and I have never seen this kind of fish," Nadia said when Vera returned to the house with her treasure. Turning the slippery fish from side to side, she said wonderingly, "This is a different species altogether from the ones I have seen before."

The fish were delicious. Using a precious bit of butter that evening, Nadia fried the three fish until the meat was steaming white and the outside turned a golden brown. As the three enjoyed the savory fish, Vera explained to Uncle Viktor how God had provided the treat.

"I just dipped into the water with my sieve, and immediately there was a fish inside it," she shouted into his ear. "Then I did it two more times, and each time I had a fish. God sent fish to us, Uncle Viktor. We are very thankful for that!"

Uncle Viktor mulled over the words that had been shouted into his ear. As he slowly looked from Vera to the fish bones on his plate, a smile played around the corners of his mouth. "Praise the Lord," he said shakily. "This manna sure tastes like fish!"

Vera and Nadia laughed at the old man's words, rejoicing in his clarity of mind.

Vera found herself amazed at the look on her mother's face as Nadia laughed at Uncle Viktor's joke. How wonderful to see the love that God had brought into their home! The spirit of heaviness and oppression was gone. Instead, they were surrounded by a harmony the old house had never known before.

Manna.

The moment she woke up the next morning, the word came to Vera. "Thank you, God, for the fish," she whispered gratefully. "Thank you for allowing us to be the recipients of your kindness."

Manna. It rang through Vera's mind. She began thinking about the story she had heard in church of God's provision for the Israelites during their journey to Canaan. "Their journey was like our walk here on earth," the pastor had said. "Daily, God provided the Israelites with manna. He still provides us with spiritual food and gives us eternal life. We open ourselves to Him every day, and every day He gives us new inspiration and comfort. We cannot store it up, just like the people walking through the desert couldn't store the manna. He wants to give us fresh food every day."

"Yes, God," Vera said aloud. "I want your freshness every day. I cannot live on past experiences. I want to hear from you today."

Fish. Manna. Somehow there seemed to be a connection between the two in her mind. Was God speaking to her? Vera stilled herself. She reflected on the awe that she had felt yesterday when she realized that God had provided the fish. The sense of His presence had been so real.

Daily. The message would not cease. Vera could feel the need to act rising up in her. "God, do you want me to go get more fish? Are you telling me that you will send some today too? Like daily manna?"

Eagerly Vera got dressed. Her back ached as it often did in the morning but as usual, she ignored it. Pain was such a constant companion that it never surprised her anymore.

The sieve, now clean, was hanging on a hook above the worktable in the kitchen. Vera put on her coat, used the broom handle to push the sieve off the high hook, caught it neatly as it fell, and went outside into the sharp morning air.

It took her just as long as usual to traverse the distance from the house to the stream, but today Vera felt an urgency to get there quickly.

"I want to believe, God. I do not want to come out here and look foolish, but I think you spoke to me. I want to learn to hear your voice. I keep hearing *manna* and *fish*. I do believe you are talking to me."

The sideways slide down the bank was not any easier than it had been the day before, but Vera did not mind. The water swirled around the pool as usual. Thin, lacy edges of ice lined the stream.

Vera took a deep breath, steadied herself, and dipped way down deep, as far as the handle would allow her to.

She felt it almost immediately—the vibrating sensation that told her something was inside her sieve again. As she drew her makeshift net from the water, she saw it. Another fish! The same kind she had caught yesterday.

Once more Vera felt holy awe sweeping over her, and she began praising her Lord. She placed the fish in the hole, and with another wild sweep, she dipped once more.

Another fish! The third try came up empty, as did the fourth and the fifth. Apparently no more fish were coming to her that morning.

The next day she caught three fish again in quick succession. The following day, the fish were smaller, but there were four.

No one in the village had ever seen such fish. No one could identify them. That did not matter to the grateful trio who received them. As far as they were concerned, these were manna fish. All winter they had fish soup, fried fish, and fish patties.

"God, truly now I see how you provide for two old people and a crippled woman," Vera prayed. "I worship you with all of my heart. Of course, I would worship you even if you didn't give us fish. I love you simply because you are so good, but I do worship you for your kindness to us. Thank you, Jesus."

Changes 14

"You are an invalid, so you should be getting a pension," the neighbor lady told Vera. "The government promised all disabled people a monthly amount of money. Our constitution promises that all the elderly, the handicapped, and the disabled will be provided for."

"I don't know anything about that," Vera said doubtfully, turning to look at the speaker. "How would I even apply?"

"You just go to that woman who is authorized by the government to oversee the affairs of our village and tell her."

It all sounded so simple, yet Vera was hesitant to embark on such a venture. Could it be as easy as it sounded?

"You take any medical records you have with you," the neighbor continued. "They will review your status, and after they approve you, they will give you a monthly pension. You need it. Your mother is not strong anymore, and your old uncle cannot last much longer. Then what will you do?"

"I will trust in God to provide," Vera replied, her mind flying to the daily fish God was still giving them.

"Humph," the neighbor woman sniffed. "You and your mother always manage to say something that sounds so religious."

The woman in the bleak, colorless office looked dismissively at Vera over the top of her glasses and then turned back to the papers in her hand.

"We need a doctor's verification that you are an invalid," she said in a cold and distant voice.

"Do you think I am stooped over like this for no reason at all?" Vera asked. "It would seem to me that anyone can see quite easily that I am crippled. It was not easy for me to get here. To see a doctor, I would have to go on the bus to Khmilnyk and back again to your office. Can you not verify that I am indeed an invalid?"

Pushing the documents from past doctor visits back to Vera, the directress merely said, "That is not my problem. No current doctor's statement, no application."

Vera did not leave immediately. "So do you think I will be accepted as an invalid and granted a pension? My mother is not strong and can hardly work, and we have an elderly uncle living with us. We are having difficulty finding enough food for us to eat."

Raising her voice, the directress said again, "That is not my problem. You will go now."

Vera took the papers and turned to leave. She could feel the woman's unfriendly stare following her shuffling walk out of the room.

"There is the doctor's statement." Vera was back in the government office two weeks later.

Without a word the directress briefly scanned the document. Then she studied it more carefully, occasionally directing sharp glances at Vera, as though the woman in front of her might be trying to commit fraud.

"May I sit down?" Vera asked, resting one hand on a wooden chair in front of the desk. Only silence met her request, so Vera sat down and rested her aching back against the hard wood.

"Your application will be considered," the woman finally said.

"Do you have the power to accept or reject applications?" Vera asked politely.

Drawing herself upright, the woman looked down her nose at Vera. "I am in charge of the affairs of this village. What I say is what will happen."

"Then I am thinking you can give me an answer," Vera replied evenly.

"You are not giving me advice on how to do my job, are you?" The words were spoken with disdain.

"No, ma'am," Vera replied. "I merely thought that if you have the authority to make the decision, you could inform me of that decision today."

"For a cripple, you seem to have a sharp mind," the woman retorted. "It might be a bit too sharp for one in your position."

Vera smiled. "A disfigured basket may hold perfectly good apples."

The import of her proverb was not lost on the woman. "I will review your case," she said with a hint of softening in her tone.

"The pension!" Vera said, holding the slip of paper which promised her sixteen rubles. "God moved in that woman's heart, and I am now getting a pension!"

Nadia had to see the paper for herself, and they tried to shout the good news to Uncle Viktor. Although he smiled at them, Vera was not sure that he understood. More and more he was spending his days in bed.

"Come on, Uncle," Nadia said. "It's time for you to go outside." Through experience she had learned that if she failed to take the old man to the outhouse regularly, she had the far more unpleasant task of cleaning up after him.

The next day Vera made her daily trek to the river for fish. Even though she dipped again and again, for the first time in months, no fish were in the sieve.

"Nothing this morning," she told her mother upon returning to the house.

"There will be no more," Nadia said matter-of-factly. "God has been giving us fish for . . . let's see . . . about nine months. Now He made it possible for you to get the pension, and that will help provide for our needs."

Nadia's prophecy was accurate. Vera caught no more fish in the stream, and even though she checked periodically for a while, the supply had indeed dried up.

"I see, God, that you do provide," Vera said gratefully. "Sometimes it is by means of manna fish, and other times through the government."

"I want to be baptized," Nadia told the pastor.

Pavel looked at the two women, mother and daughter. "We will need to interview you," he explained, looking at Vera and remembering her request seven years earlier.

"All right," Nadia agreed. She knew about the interviews the pastors conducted. "How soon can I be baptized after that?"

Pavel looked out the window at the bare trees of late autumn. "We will need to wait until next spring when it warms up. The water is too cold for a baptism this time of year."

Nadia gripped the edge of the pew until her knuckles turned white. Then she spoke firmly, "You are not the one being baptized. You only need to go into the water up to your waist. I am the one asking for baptism, because I want to be obedient to God. I don't mind being baptized in icy cold water. Next spring might be too late. Please, I want to do it now."

Pavel marveled at the woman's faith and courage. "Yes, my sister, we will interview you very soon. If you have a clear testimony, we will honor your wishes."

Nadia was the only applicant on the cold night when she was baptized, but as she confidently answered the pastor's questions and was lowered into the frigid waters, the warmth of the Spirit filled her. She told Vera later, "Now I know that whatever happens to me, it is well with my soul. Jesus has saved me, and now I have given my testimony and sealed it with baptism. I feel at peace in my heart."

Vera remembered her mother's words and took comfort from them when, later that winter, Nadia became ill. After only a few weeks in bed, she passed away.

The days of preparation for the funeral were difficult ones for Vera, for she had grown to love her mother and knew she would miss her sorely. The ladies from the church were very kind and came to the house to assist Vera with anything she needed. Uncle Viktor was too weak to leave his bed; indeed, he hardly seemed aware of what was going on.

Like the believers did whenever they had an opportunity to witness and preach the Gospel, they sang songs of praise and worship as they carried Nadia's body to the cemetery. The village people who attended the funeral were surprised at the life and energy the believers put into their songs.

The Spirit comforted Vera's aching heart, and she rested in the care of Jesus. How she rejoiced each time she remembered the beginning of her own walk with God and the consequent decision her mother had made to follow the Lord.

"Mama seemed to have known that her end was near," she told one of the ladies from church. "She felt an urgent need to be baptized last fall, even though it was so cold. She died in peace, knowing she had been obedient to God."

Uncle Viktor's tired old body grew steadily weaker. One morning, six months after Nadia's death, Vera went to minister to his needs and found his lifeless body. He, too, had died peacefully. As they buried him in the cemetery, the warm summer sun shone on the soil where Nadia's body was also buried. Yes, Vera's loved ones were gone, but as Pavel spoke about the coming resurrection of the dead, she had joy deep in her heart.

In spite of the difficulty she had experienced in caring for Viktor during Nadia's illness and after her death, Vera mourned her great-uncle's passing with heartfelt sorrow. He had been the vessel God had used to bring her to an understanding of salvation in Jesus. Yes, it had been a wearisome task for the crippled girl to care for the elderly man's needs during his final months, but she had done it joyfully.

"You will be all alone," her concerned friends from church reminded Vera after Viktor's funeral, and Pavel asked if she would be all right by herself.

"I will never be alone," Vera told her friends with conviction. "I have Jesus for my constant and loving companion. The government is sending my pension, and I have my garden and the hens. God is good to this unworthy daughter of His."

Her church family prayed with her and then left, knowing the faith that God had given Vera was going to sustain her.

"Yes, God, it's just you and me now," Vera said aloud. "You are my Father, my mother, and my entire family. You are my Saviour, my friend, and my constant companion."

The house did seem empty, and at times Vera felt acutely lonely. Yet she always knew the joy of the Comforter's presence.

Bread From Heaven 15

Vera carefully counted the money in her purse. Thirty kopeks. It was all she had, and her pension would not arrive for two more weeks.

She sighed, and as was her habit now that she lived by herself, she spoke her thoughts out loud. "Easter, the resurrection of Jesus, is celebrated tomorrow. Thankfully, it will cost me only ten kopeks for the bus fare to church, but there will be no Easter supper for this girl." She swept the remaining coins into a pile and dumped them into her purse.

Vera clutched the wall as she hobbled into her kitchen. On some days her back bothered her more than usual, and today was such a day. "At least I can walk," she reminded herself. "If I couldn't walk, I would be in some mental institution." She shuddered as she remembered one such place her mother had taken her to visit a friend when Vera was a small girl.

"Why have you allowed such suffering?" Vera asked God as she pulled two potatoes from the pail behind the curtain of her worktable. "I don't understand. I cannot think it was you who sent all the pain and suffering that the poor souls endure in the institutions. It must come from Satan."

Vera's pragmatic view of life was based on what she had experienced. "I feel that even my own crippled body is the attack of Satan against what God wants me to accomplish, but I will not be stopped by my crippled body. I will still do everything I possibly can for God."

Sinking onto a wooden chair, Vera began peeling the wrinkled potatoes carefully, making sure she barely skimmed off the skins. Nothing
could go to waste. Even the skins were carefully saved for the three
chickens she still had.

Life had become more difficult for Vera since she lived by herself. Her
pension barely kept her alive, and by the time she paid her electric bill,
she had almost no money left to buy food. She spent many tedious hours
trudging to and from the wooded area on the other side of the village
pond to gather sticks and branches to cook what little food she did have.

"Lord, you have been my dwelling place," Vera sang as she prepared
her meager meal. "You have been the refuge for my soul, and in you,
only in you, will I trust."

Her involvement with the church had made a huge impact on Vera's
life. The sermons, the songs, and the sincere love had already healed
many of the seeking woman's wounds. "I will trust and believe. Jesus,
you are the joy of my heart!" Peace and gladness came to rest in Vera's
heart as she sang.

"Christ arose!"

"Truly, He arose!"

The traditional Easter greetings had been given and responded to all
day. This was one day when everyone, believers and unbelievers, greeted
each other with the glorious words. True, there were thousands who
used these terms merely as a Ukrainian tradition, but for Vera and the
believers who had met in Khmilnyk, the joyous greetings resonated
deeply in their hearts. This was the reason for their hope. Jesus was alive
and living in the heart of every true believer!

The stirring songs, the inspired message, and the love feast they shared
together after the service—everything had been profoundly meaning-
ful to Vera.

"We will come and visit with you the rest of the afternoon," Maria
told Vera as they waited for the bus. "My son and his friends love to

sing, and I know you will enjoy their songs."

"I would like that," Vera replied gratefully. "I was wishing for a chance to learn the words of the last song the choir sang this morning. It touched me deeply, and I want to learn it."

Even while she was saying the welcoming words, panic was gripping her mind. What would she feed her visitors? It was unthinkable to have guests and not offer them food, but her cupboard was bare.

"Yuri," Maria spoke to her teenage son who was waiting beside them, along with his friend Sasha, "let's stop in and spend the evening with Vera. She wants to learn the words to the song the choir sang this morning."

"Sure," the boys agreed pleasantly, "we'll do that."

Vera felt torn. She desperately wanted to have the guests come and stay with her. Maria had always taken a keen interest in her, and Vera felt comfortable with the kindly lady. It was Maria who had more than once pressed a few kopeks, and even at times a ruble, into Vera's hand, firmly ignoring the objections Vera had felt obligated to raise. Maria's generous spirit spoke volumes to her young friend.

Vera took a mental inventory. Some of the potatoes from the day before were still in the cooking pot, along with some onions she had been using sparingly. But that meager fare was nothing to feed her guests! She did not even have a crust of bread in the house. At the same time, she could not refuse the fellowship.

As the bus lumbered along, stopping at crossroads to drop off passengers and pick up others, Maria chatted easily with her worried friend. The bus was full of people all dressed in their best clothes for the holiday.

Lord, I don't mind running out of food for myself, Vera found herself praying silently. *But I can't serve that bland stew to my guests! I have nothing to serve with it! There is no bread or anything in my house!*

"The police have been following the activities of the believers more closely," Maria was saying. "We also think the Orthodox priests are becoming more alarmed as people are repenting and leaving their churches. The revival has made an impact on many villages."

The bus stopped and Vera and the other three got off. Maria considerately matched her steps to Vera's slower pace as the boys walked beside them. As they traversed the cobbles into her village, Vera kept praying silently, *Lord, please show me what to do.*

At the pond the boys stopped to watch a long-legged heron that was fishing in the reeds. They were rewarded when the heron darted his head into the water, his long, slender neck shooting out with amazing speed. When the heron's head resurfaced, it was holding a small fish.

The women reached Vera's gate, and Maria walked around the back to the outhouse. Vera hobbled to the front door and, without looking, reached to the back of a shelf beside the door where she normally hid the key to her house. Her searching fingers were impeded by a bulky package. She straightened herself as far as she could, and as her eyes rested on the shelf, she felt a rush of adrenaline sweep through her.

Somehow she knew in her heart what she was going to find in those packages even before she opened the first one. There were three packages on the shelf, all wrapped neatly in brown store paper. Vera pulled the first one down and unwrapped it. Sure enough, it was bread—a huge round loaf of crusty bread, the best the village bakery sold!

"Oh, Lord! Thank you." Vera felt her knees grow weak, and she sat down on the wooden bench. Tears began to roll down her cheeks as she gazed at the bread.

"Are you all right?" Maria asked with concern as she saw Vera's tears.

"Look what God has sent," Vera replied, smiling through her tears. "I had nothing to offer you except some of yesterday's potatoes, and God has sent me this wonderful bread."

Immediately Maria understood why her young friend had seemed preoccupied on the journey home. "Oh, Vera," she said kindly, "I had no idea you were worrying about that. We would have been quite content without food."

"There is more," Vera replied quietly, pointing to the shelf.

Maria took the second package from the shelf and removed the brown paper from it. Vera cried out with joy when she saw the generous roll of kielbasa it contained.

"And cheese!" Maria said exultantly as she opened the third package.

That evening was one of the most memorable of Vera's life as she sliced the bread and meat and cheese and served it to her guests. She joyfully insisted that they eat plenty. When several of the neighbors came over to listen to the singing, Vera served them food as well. "God has generously given us this food. He meant it for you as well as for me," she insisted. After they had spent the evening singing, she even tried to send along the leftover food with her visitors.

"No, Vera," Maria firmly told her. "You keep this food. I know you need it."

The loaf was only half gone, and the next morning Vera cut a big slice for her breakfast. That afternoon she shared some with the girl who had brought her water from the village well. And that evening another big slice of bread with the last of the potatoes made a very satisfying supper for her.

The next morning, knife in hand to slice off another piece, Vera stopped in surprise and peered at the loaf. "It appears to be the same size it was on Sunday evening," she said in amazement. The large loaf lay on the cutting board, inviting Vera to partake in its wholesome goodness.

Vera continued eating from the loaf of bread for several days with no noticeable decrease in the size of the loaf. Not until the day her pension money arrived at the post office did she finally eat the last crust. It was still as delicious and fresh-tasting as the day it had mysteriously arrived on her shelf.

"It was a miracle," Vera said in reflection. "Not only was it a miracle that it appeared on my shelf, but also a miracle that the cats didn't get into it, and that it was such good food."

Grinning mischievously, she asked, "God, did you send it using ravens, like you did for Elijah? Or did you send an angel, telling him to wait until I was almost home to prevent the cats from getting it? Well, it doesn't matter. I marvel at how you love me and how you look after this crippled girl whom you have adopted. I do feel loved by you. Thank you."

More than once Vera shared the wonderful story with the village women. "You have laughed at me and said that all my prayers accomplished nothing. Now look at how God has answered my prayers. He sent me this food just when I needed it most."

"I have prayed for help, and nothing ever happened to me," a skeptical neighbor told her. "You can pray until you wear holes in your knees, and nothing actually changes."

"The priest is the only one who knows how to pray the right way," another chimed in, crossing herself instinctively.

"No," Vera said confidently, "God hears the prayers of the repentant and believing. I know. I have eaten of His bread, bread from heaven."

Gifts of Love 16

"Take it. It is for you," the pastor told Vera.

"And what makes you think I can ride a bike?" Vera laughed. "I see you have faith in God if you think that. See my hunchback?" She looked skeptically at the old blue bicycle, worn but still serviceable.

"I think you can learn to ride it," Pavel told her. "We want you to have it."

"But I have no money to pay for it," Vera objected. "My chickens are not laying well right now, and my pension . . ."

Raising his hand, Pavel stopped her. "No, Vera. It is a gift. We are not asking money for the bike."

Vera stared at the bike as Pavel steadied it with his hand. "How will I get it home?" she asked.

"I will see if I can get Yuri to ride it to your house for you, and then he can come back on the bus."

The first attempts at bike riding were not easy. Vera fell more than once, but eventually, with sore knees and scraped arms, she learned to ride. Her curved back made it difficult to lift her head far enough to see ahead, but she learned to tilt her head to one side to see reasonably well. In spite of the difficulties, she was very grateful for the new freedom her wheels brought to her.

The afternoon sun shone on the young woman's back as she bent over, balancing her bicycle. Vera pedaled steadily on the blacktop road that led from Khmilnyk back to her house.

She was on her way home from church, and since the weather had changed, she felt sure she could bike that distance and save a few kopeks. In reality, there were no kopeks to save, for once again her pension had not lasted through the month.

Vera had not eaten that morning. The night before, she had eaten a few small potatoes and a thin slice of bread. She was saving her loaf, mentally calculating how long it would have to last her.

"Lord, I pray that the hens will lay well so I can sell the eggs for another loaf of bread," Vera prayed out loud. The road seemed to wobble. Vera closed one eye to focus better. The front tire of her bicycle wobbled ominously.

The drone of a crop-dusting airplane far above hardly entered her consciousness. For days already the pilots had been flying their airplanes over the fields, fighting the insects with pesticide.

On the way to church that morning, Vera had seen five big trucks parked in a semicircle beside the road. A dozen or more workers had been cooking over fires, and it was evident they had set up camp there. Apparently the men had been hauling the pesticides and fuel needed for the crop dusters.

Now, as Vera came closer to the same spot, she saw that the trucks were gone. However, it was evident that the men had not cleaned up their camp site. Garbage littered the space where the trucks had been parked.

"I will see whether they left anything for the cripple," Vera said and steered her bike across to the littered area.

Vera thought it truly amazing what treasures were discarded as worthless by the more fortunate. More than once while in Khmilnyk, Vera had searched through the trash bins and retrieved bits and pieces of food. True, many times the food was too spoiled or rotten to use, but Vera was not easily discouraged. She learned that wilted cabbage leaves can be stripped away until the heart is reached. Dirty portions of bread can be cut off and the stale inside toasted over flame. She thought it quite possible that the workers at this camp site might have tossed out something that she could eat.

"Aha!" Vera stopped her bicycle and steadied herself on one foot. Carefully she dismounted and lowered the bike to the ground.

At the edge of the campfire, where it was obvious the workers had cooked their food, she found a whole loaf of bread tossed to one side. "I beat the dogs to this," she chortled gleefully and slipped it into her bag.

She began methodically checking out the other litter. Not surprisingly, it consisted mostly of empty bottles of vodka. Then she spotted a package wrapped in brown paper of the type used by butchers to wrap meat.

Eagerly Vera bent over and removed the top of the paper. There was meat inside! She removed the rest of the paper. In front of her eyes lay more meat than she had ever seen in one package. It was mostly fat, to be sure, but it was streaked with red meat too.

Looking around to make sure she was alone, Vera scanned the road. No one was in sight.

"Lord, this is truly amazing," she said breathlessly. "How is it possible that so much meat was left behind?" She tried to picture the men loading up their possessions and driving off without remembering their supply of pork fat.

Visions of potatoes fried in fat, of bread toasted and moistened with fried pork drippings, and of borsch with actual pieces of pork in it came to her with mouth-watering clarity. Oh, how could such wealth have fallen into her possession?

"God, is this you again?" Vera asked, circling the package and staring at it as though it might disappear before her eyes. "Have you made the men forget this package so I can have it?"

That the bread had escaped scavengers like dogs or crows was amazing, but the fact that the meat was untouched was even more amazing. Crows were always circling in the air overhead, waiting for people to leave their cooking spots for even an instant. They would swoop in quickly to pilfer anything edible, and yet here there was food, and it was all intact.

"Is it really for me?" Vera asked the question honestly. She did not want to take what did not belong to her. Once more she looked in all directions. There was no sign of the trucks, and not even the distant sound of airplanes. The workers were gone for good. Nothing else of any value was left there. It was clear they had no intentions of returning.

"What will they do when they realize they left their meat behind?" Vera murmured to herself. "Will they return to hunt for it?"

The answer came clearly. No, of course they would not drive back for a piece of meat. They would naturally rationalize that some scavenger had already made off with it.

Without further hesitation, Vera bent over to lift the package. It was not easy to tie the heavy parcel securely on her bike, and it was particularly difficult to balance the bicycle and ride on down the road with the extra weight. In spite of the difficulty, Vera was propelled all the way home by the sheer joy that coursed through her as she rejoiced in God's provision. More than once, as she bounced over the cobbled village streets and then down the dirt road to her house, she had to stop and readjust her package.

Resting after her exhausting ordeal, Vera gazed incredulously at the huge package of meat. "I will can it," she finally decided. "It will keep a long time that way."

That evening Vera fried her potatoes with the pork fat. The delicious aroma almost made her giddy with delight. She trimmed away the dirty crust from the bread and fried it too.

"God, here is your princess! I am truly blessed in my castle, enjoying such a feast. Thank you, my Father. You look after your children in the strangest ways!"

All the next day Vera worked at canning the meat. With a feeling of reverent awe, she counted her jars at the end of the day. "Thank you, Lord, for caring for your crippled daughter," she said again. "Nineteen small jars of meat are even better than money in my purse."

——— ——— ——— ———

Vera had gathered the sticks into a bundle, and now she tied them to her bicycle. Her bundle was painfully small, for other villagers hunting fuel to burn in their stoves also frequented the woods. She found precious little firewood left within her reach.

The trip home was daunting for Vera. She knew how precarious it always was when she rode her bike, especially with a bundle of wood sticking out on both sides. "Lord, help me get back safely," she prayed.

More than once she had to get off her bike and push her load up an incline. Even though the landscape was only mildly rolling, every uphill slope made her trek harder.

At last she entered the final stretch into the village where the land was level, and with relief she began riding down between the village houses. But almost immediately a truck blocked the road. Vera sighed wearily and stopped, putting her right foot on the road to balance herself.

"But I can't use it!" Natasha, the agitated woman in front of her, was saying to the truck driver. "I am moving, and the new owners are connecting to the gas line to heat the house."

Vera checked to see what the truck was carrying and saw it was loaded with coal.

"But I can't take it back," the young driver was objecting. "They sent me here to deliver it, and I have to unload it."

Vera understood his dilemma. He would surely be in trouble if some boss sent him to deliver coal and he returned with the load. Never mind if it was even paid for. It probably had already been entered into the books as paid, and perhaps it was even paid. The gigantic bureaucracy of the communist system only functioned in a certain way, and any deviation, however logical, was not well received.

"I didn't even order all that," the woman said unhappily, coming around to the back of the truck. Then she saw Vera. "You have the wrong house anyway," Natasha said with sudden inspiration, facing Vera and putting one finger to her lips. "You have to deliver it a little farther down the road."

The driver looked bewildered at the sudden change in tactics.

"Yes, come. I will show you!" Natasha yelled at him. "Get in the truck and drive on to the house with the unpainted fence. I will be there to show you where to put it."

"I am going to give the coal to you," Natasha told Vera as the engine roared to life. "I am moving, and I can't use it. If it is dumped here, someone will just sell it for vodka money anyway. You need it more than anyone else, Vera, being a hunchback and all."

So that was that. Vera would have coal enough for the coming winter.

Natasha was already gone, hurrying out the gate after the truck, directing the driver to dump it in Vera's yard. Moments later she bustled back to her own home to get ready for her move. Then the truck was gone, the bewildered driver hardly knowing what had just happened.

"Lord, here you go again," Vera chuckled. "I pray, asking for your help, and then I get answers from you in ways I would never, ever expect. Wow, look at that mountain of coal!"

She untied her bundle of sticks and threw them against the henhouse beside the pile of coal. Black gold that coal was to Vera, worth more than gold, for it would heat her house and cook her food.

That night a terrific thunderstorm crashed upon the village. As the thunder rolled across the heavens and the lightning flashed, Vera's heart was light and rejoicing. "Lord, I used to be afraid of storms," she reminded Him. "Now I hear your voice in the thunder, and I see your glory in the flashes of lightning. You are the Almighty God. In you I put my trust. You see the needs of your child, and as Pavel says, you are a Father to the orphan. You have remembered me, your poor crippled daughter, with mercy."

And with the celestial orchestra rumbling around her, Vera lifted her voice in song. Praises poured out of her grateful heart as she sang of the loving-kindness and mercy of her King.

The Feast 17

The water was boiling. First Vera dissolved two cubes of bouillon that she had bought at the market. Then she dipped two cups of oatmeal out of the tin and dumped it into the hot water. She put a lid on the pan and pushed it to the back of the stove.

"I know I have an onion here somewhere," Vera said to herself. "I have saved this onion for something special, and I can't think of anything more special than having my church family coming here for a service."

At last she found the final onion in the bucket behind the potatoes. She squeezed it, and to her delight, it was still firm.

"Always the tears run," she sniffed, wiping her streaming eyes with her sleeve as she sliced the onion into rings and chopped the rings into smaller pieces. The onion sizzled in the hot fat as Vera browned the pieces. When they were done, she pushed the skillet to the back of the stove and checked the pot of melted lard.

Tiny bubbles rising to the top indicated that the oil was getting hot, so Vera continued her preparations. She broke two eggs into a bowl and beat the eggs together.

Now at last it was time to rest. Vera sank down on her chair in the kitchen and folded her hands together for a moment.

Ah, God was so good to her! She had such an abundance of food right now, and the long winter was almost over. She still had plenty of potatoes. The hens were laying enough for her to use several eggs for herself and still sell some at the market. Her meager pension provided bread and paid for her electricity. By taking good care of her few clothes, she was warmly clothed.

"Oh, Jesus, you have been my constant companion. It's been eight years since Mama and Uncle Viktor went to be with you, and every year you have faithfully remembered your princess in her castle."

It was her little joke. "My Father is the King, I am His daughter, and so that makes me a princess," she would explain whenever anyone asked why she referred to herself as a princess. "The princess lives in the King's house, and so my home is a castle."

Almost forty years old by now, Vera had attracted the attention of many in her village. "The crazy hunchback" became known for her tales of God's provision for her. She spoke openly of talking with God and of hearing His voice. The neighbors were treated to stories of heavenly visions and visitors. Her vivid descriptions were believed by some and passed off as the overly excited imagination of a lonely woman by others.

Pulling herself up from her chair, Vera now spooned the oatmeal mixture into the bowl with the eggs and stirred the stiff batter. A spoonful of black pepper and a little bit of salt would enhance the spices in the bouillon. She dumped in the fried onion, making sure it was distributed throughout the stiff batter. Then, taking a small lump in her hands, she formed a cake.

The oil was hot, so she dropped the first patty into it and watched with a critical eye as the cake sizzled and gently sank into the oil. As it fried, it rose to the surface, and at just the right time, Vera turned it over with a fork. When both sides were fried a beautiful brown, she removed the cake and put it in a pan.

The kitchen was warm and smelled of the frying oat cakes as Vera continued frying the small, hand-shaped cakes one by one. They would keep warm inside the clay oven until the service was over and they were ready to eat.

The big pot of borsch was already made, and she had even bought some cookies at the store. "Thank you, Lord, for supplying me with enough to share."

Nineteen people gathered in Vera's little house that evening. Sitting on every available chair and on makeshift benches, her friends from church, along with several neighbors, crowded inside.

The songs, the testimonies, and the sermon that Brother Pavel preached were all a tremendous encouragement to Vera. She was so blessed by the group of ten young people who had come to sing songs. When one of the girls gave her a handwritten copy of the new songs, Vera's heart overflowed with gratefulness.

She looked at the three neighbor ladies she had persuaded to come in spite of their apprehension at the thought of a religious service not held in a church building. Their stoic faces showed little feeling, and Vera wondered what was going on in their minds. "Lord, speak to them as only you can," she breathed.

One of the hardest things Vera had to bear was the fact she was the only believer in the entire village since her mother and Uncle Victor had died. The rest of the people seemed to be either trapped in the grip of the pointless traditions and rituals that the Orthodox Church had per- petrated for centuries, or they were atheists.

"Do not despair when your labors bear no immediate results," Pavel said at that moment, his sermon meshing with Vera's thoughts. "The work that you do out of love for Jesus will never go unnoticed by Him. Remember, even as you do these good works for others, you are doing it unto Jesus."

Vera listened gratefully to the encouraging words coming from her pastor. She remembered how reluctant he had seemed to baptize her when she was a new Christian. At the time, she had wondered why it was so, but in the following years she had found out that the elders were facing extreme pressure from the police. Under that duress they had wanted to make sure that anyone they baptized was truly a believer. More than once someone had pretended to be repentant, only to bring the police to the scene of the baptism to arrest the ones who were con- ducting "illegal" activities.

At services in Khmilnyk, the believers constantly prayed for the pastors who had been arrested and sent away to Siberia for preaching the Gospel and conducting baptisms. These were trying times as the government in Moscow had determined to erase religion out of the Soviet Union once and for all. They really believed they could show the entire world how successfully the communist system met the needs of human beings.

"In spite of any persecution, if our communion with God stays fresh, we will have the strength to remain faithful and true to Him," Pavel continued. "Many have been tried for their faith, and I rejoice to say that most have remained true to Jesus. He has not given us anything that is too difficult to bear."

Vera found herself wondering how much Pavel himself had suffered. She knew he often traveled to preach in other cities and villages. She had learned to appreciate his sincerity and godly example as he served his congregation.

"O Lord my God! When I in awesome wonder, Consider all the worlds thy hands have made . . ."

The youth choir sang harmoniously, their voices woven into a tapestry of sound that thrilled Vera's heart.

"Then sings my soul, my Saviour God, to Thee! How great thou art! How great thou art!" Vera joined her voice with the others. Singing was a wonderful vent for the deep joy that surged up from deep inside her.

The choir sang four more songs; then they all stood for prayer. One by one they spoke to God, voicing their praise and requests as they were led.

———

"Vera, this is absolutely delicious!" Still another person complimented Vera on her fried oatcakes. "What meat did you use?"

Vera laughed. "This meat was raised in the oat field," she quipped, her eyes crinkling in laughter. "The spices and fried onions are what make it flavorful."

Several of the women and girls had brought a fruit drink called *kompot* with them, and as they sat around the tables they had made with boards stretched from box to box, the believers enjoyed their love feast tremendously.

Vera watched as the three neighbor ladies thawed under the warm friendliness of her church family and began talking more freely. "Lord, let them see the love you put into the hearts of your children," she prayed. "Oh, Jesus, I pray for their salvation. Let them find the joy I have found in being your daughter."

"I have a family," Vera said gratefully to her guests as they prepared to leave into the dark night. "The family of God is one of the greatest gifts I have received since I began my walk with the Lord. Thank you all for coming to share cheer and inspiration with the princess in her castle. What would I do without my Christian brothers and sisters?"

"Sister," Pavel said as he and his wife bent over to shake hands with the small woman, "you are a constant blessing to the rest of us in the church. Your faithfulness and love for God inspire many who are struggling in their walk with Christ. Though small in body, you are a giant in the faith."

Ludmilla bent over and kissed each of Vera's cheeks lovingly. "Oh, Vera, keep that love for Jesus burning brightly in your heart! You truly are a princess, and the beauty that shines inside you shows right through your eyes for all to see."

"Even a marred basket can hold treasured fruit," Vera said humbly. "I have Jesus living inside me, so whatever good you think you see in me is only a picture of Him."

That night, Vera spent a long time on her knees. The floor was as hard as it had always been, the pain as constant as ever, and yet the things of earth were strangely dim as the glory and presence of the Comforter flooded her soul. The glory of God was so real, and the presence of Jesus so strong, that any sense of time melted away as she communed with the One whom she loved more than anything else.

These moments of worship in the very presence of God were what Vera lived for. For countless solitary hours, this woman, who had known such incredible pain and loneliness, was ushered into supernatural places. Like Paul, she was caught up, not certain whether in the body or out of the body, to sit in heavenly places.

She was largely unconscious of the tremendous impact her faith made on other believers, so it was always a surprise for her when people blessed her for encouraging them with her life.

"I'm just a crippled princess in her castle, serving her Master. I'm doing what any rescued and restored servant would do for the One who brought hope and peace to a sad and neglected life. Whatever little things I can do for God are only a small token of my eternal thankfulness and love for Him." With a smile that lit up her entire face, and with eyes that were filled with life, Vera constantly radiated a depth of character that came from hours with the Master.

The Priest 18

"Vera, come sit down," Larissa called. "You can share the meal with us."

Vera had been riding her bike home when she had seen the crowd of people at the end of the street. Larissa's aged mother had died, and now that the funeral was over, all the relatives were gathered in Larissa's yard for a meal. The tables were spread along the front of the house, and the people were seated under the spreading grape arbor, shielded from the hot sun.

"Well, I suppose," Vera replied doubtfully. "Are you sure you have enough space for me?"

"Oh, Vera, as little as you are, we can fit you in anywhere." Larissa's big voice matched her size. "Come, come, we have plenty of food."

"Lord," Vera prayed silently, "let me be a witness for you in this group."

The noisy crowd had already begun eating when Vera arrived. "Sit right here at the end of this bench. Scoot on down and make room for Vera," Larissa directed.

The man in black who was seated at the end of the table was the new village priest. He was presiding over the meal and eating heartily as the food was pressed on him. The fried potatoes and *vareniki* and *perogi* were all delicious. Vera had not eaten such food in a long time.

"Give the old lady some wine." The priest raised his voice to address

Larissa as he pointed at Vera's glass. Then he lifted his own empty glass. "Mine needs refilling too," he said. "Even though I have had two glasses already, you know the Bible says that God loves trinity."

Everyone but Vera laughed. As Larissa filled the priest's glass for the third time, she told him, "Ah, but Vera doesn't drink wine. She is a believer."

The priest turned for a closer look at the slight figure beside him. "Oh, I thought you were old because you are bent over," he said mockingly. "Now I see that you are not really an old woman."

Vera smiled. "No, I am not old." Then she lifted her eyes to look straight into Nicolai's face. "Where in the Bible does it say, 'God loves trinity'?" The words were out of her mouth before she realized what she was doing.

"Eh? We have a smart woman here even though she is a cripple?" The priest's voice was slurred already, and he turned to look curiously at Vera. Vera could smell vodka in addition to the wine on his breath.

"Vera!" Larissa hissed.

The conversation at their end of the table died down abruptly.

With a loud hiccup Nicolai said, "I believe it is time to end this meal." He swayed in his chair.

Vera clapped her hand over her mouth. Without another word she slipped off the bench and went to get her bicycle. "God, why did I say that?" she asked on the way home. "What made me ask the priest that? Did you prompt me to speak, or was that my own thought?"

Vera was learning to be much more conscious of the leading of the Spirit in her speech with other people. She truly wanted every word and action to be directed by God.

She sensed no response to her question. "I think I said that on my own," Vera admitted reluctantly. "I really want to hear only your voice, God. Like Jesus said, 'I only say the things I hear the Father say.' That is what I want, Lord. Please forgive me for my hasty reply. Let it be your voice and not mine."

"Speak to him again. Explain why you asked that question." The words came simply and clearly into Vera's mind.

"You are asking me to give my testimony?" she asked aloud. "To the priest?"

She was not well acquainted with Nicolai. He had come to replace Volodya some time ago, and since Vera never attended any of the Orthodox services anymore, she did not know the new priest. Was God really asking her to witness to him?

"How can I? He only knows me as the 'old' crippled woman. He probably won't even remember me after he dries out."

But the impression that she needed to witness to the priest did not go away. Vera pondered over the message she had received. At last she said, "Okay, God. If you bring him into my life again, I will speak to him. I don't know what I will say, but you have asked me to witness to him, so I will depend on you to give me the words." After a pause she added, "At least I will if I ever have the opportunity to speak to him, which is not likely."

The months rolled by and occasionally Vera did see Nicolai at a distance, striding along in his black robes, but the opportunity to speak to him did not come.

"Vera! Halloo! It's Larissa!"

The booming voice outside the garden gate announced the visitor.

"I'm out here," Vera called.

Larissa rounded the corner of the house and joined Vera in the garden where she was digging her potato crop. "My! What a bountiful crop of potatoes!" she exclaimed. "Your garden certainly produced well."

Vera straightened herself as best she could and noticed that a stranger was walking with Larissa.

"My nephew from Odessa," Larissa introduced the tall man. "Alexei came to see me. In his car," she added proudly.

Vera nodded to the young man.

Alexei stood surveying the garden. "My, what a wonderful crop of potatoes," he said admiringly. "I am envious."

"He lives in the city where fresh produce is not so easy to find," Larissa explained.

"We have our easier lives in the cities, but you have your better food," Alexei said, rubbing his hand appreciatively over his stomach.

Vera wanted to add, "But we can't even afford to eat our own food because we need money so desperately that we end up selling it." But she kept her tongue.

"Would you be willing to sell some of your potatoes to me?" Alexei asked eagerly. "Or are there more people in your house who will eat them?"

"No, I live here by myself," Vera replied. Tilting her head sideways to look up into his face, she said thoughtfully, "I'll tell you what. If you harvest my potato crop, I will let you take potatoes for your work."

"The boys and I can help," Larissa said immediately. "Alexei, that is a good bargain."

That very afternoon Vera had looked at her huge potato crop and asked God, "How will I ever harvest all these potatoes by myself?" She had decided she would have to stretch the harvest out over a number of weeks, as her back protested bitterly if she kept on working too many days without adequate rest.

"Wonderful!" Alexei was excited at the opportunity.

That evening the car pulled into Vera's courtyard. Alexei climbed out and two strong young boys jumped out after him. "My cousins and I will have those potatoes dug before dark," he said with a grin. "Larissa said she will bring her daughters to help a little later."

Alexei pulled shovels out of the trunk of the car as he continued enthusiastically, "My, won't my wife be pleased when I return with potatoes! We can store them on the balcony and have good potatoes all winter."

Vera followed the men to the garden. "Oh, Lord, watch those men," she said gratefully. "See how quickly they can do the digging? Thank you for sending them to my palace."

A moment later she heard voices, and Larissa strode into the garden, followed by her daughters. But what was this? Why was the priest coming with them?

For one ludicrous moment Vera wondered if he was going to help dig potatoes, but she stifled her grin at the very thought of the black-robed man stooping over the rows and digging.

"Alexei!" Larissa called to her nephew. "Father Nicolai wants to know if you could haul some cement bags to his house with your car."

It was common for villagers to ask for help whenever someone came to their village with a car. Alexei stopped work to discuss the matter with the priest.

"Here is your opportunity." Vera stopped in midmotion as the Voice came to her. Then she began to smile. "Praise the Lord!" She felt a strange thrill as she remembered her earlier prayer: "If you give me opportunity to speak to him, I will."

Now here was the priest, right in her own garden.

It must have been a strange sight to the workers as Vera, hunched over and barefooted, made her way across the garden to the priest, repeating, "Praise the Lord! Praise the Lord!"

Nicolai was accustomed to being greeted with deference and seemed to think that Vera's joy was due to the honor of his visit. Automatically, he extended his hand for Vera to kiss.

"You do not know why I am praising God," Vera said exultantly. "I asked God to give me an opportunity to speak to you since last spring when I sat beside you after the funeral of Larissa's mother, and now He brings you right here to my garden! That is why I am praising the Lord!"

"Vera, you are crazy!" Larissa crossed herself in alarm as Vera mentioned the funeral.

"No, I am not crazy; I'm just being obedient to what the Spirit is telling me to do," Vera smiled.

"What is it that you want?" Nicolai puckered his brow suspiciously.

"I was the one who asked where in the Bible it says, 'God loves trinity,' when you asked for the third glass of wine."

Nicolai nodded, but it was clear he did not really remember the incident. "Yes?"

"Why did you say that?" Vera asked simply.

The priest shrugged. "You know it is a common saying among our people," he replied dismissively.

Vera nodded. "And if people hear the priest say that, they will think it is written in the Bible, but it is not."

"It does not harm anyone to think it is God's Word," the priest said condescendingly.

"The Bible is filled with truth that God wants us to use in our every-day speech. If we continually treat other sayings like His Word, we are crowding out the truth that He wants us to spread. That is especially damaging when it comes from people who are looked up to as knowing the truth." Vera was not exactly sure where she was going with this, but the words seemed to come to her without effort.

"You are the priest and I am nobody," she continued humbly. "Yet, I do not hear the truth coming from your mouth. I hear you using the sayings of men as if they were God's truth. God wants you to use His sayings."

Cocking his head sideways, Nicolai smirked. "And what sayings of God should I use?" he inquired.

"For God so loved the world, that he gave his only begotten Son, that whosoever believeth in him should not perish, but have everlasting life," Vera quoted with feeling.

Nicolai's eyebrows lifted. "How is it that you know the Bible? How long have you studied?" His interest was piqued.

"For twenty years," Vera answered. "I finally have my own copy, but before that, I read the pages my great-uncle sent me when I was a teenager."

The idea occurred to Nicolai that this village woman was challenging his own knowledge of the truth. He asked, "Just how long did you go to grade school?"

"Three years, and then I was crippled in a fall from a tree and was unable to return to school," Vera told him truthfully.

"Well, I went through eleven years of school, and then I graduated from the seminary," Nicolai told her authoritatively.

"Well," Vera said, "out here in this garden, we are equals. You are not the priest, and I am not just a poor hunchback. Let me ask you, why do you take money to pray for people who have died? Why do you first require money before you go to the villagers' houses to pray for healing? Is that something you learned from God or in the seminary?" Again, she was not sure just why she was led to ask the questions she did. Someone else seemed to control her tongue.

Nicolai's eyes closed into angry slits. "You, a foolish, crippled woman, dare question the sacred traditions of the priest's way of life? You speak heresy."

Vera said nothing because she did not sense God giving her any words.

"You ignorant believers," the priest said, using the term applied to all evangelicals. "You think you are so smart and can challenge the traditions that have been in the church for hundreds of years. You know nothing!"

"We know God," Vera said softly. "We know the Bible, and we know what it is to have the Spirit of God living inside of us."

Growing angry, Nicolai threw his arm out in disgust. "Then if you are so smart, tell . . ." He looked around at the landscape and then continued, "Tell that hill to be made flat. The Bible says that if you have faith, you can command a mountain to be removed, and it will be. Go ahead, tell the hill to flatten itself out."

Vera did not wince, although the darkness she felt was not entirely due to the approaching dusk. "I don't need that hill to be flattened," she said evenly. "My neighbors would no longer have a place to graze their goats if we turned it into flat farmland."

"Your head is filled with nonsense," Nicolai said after a pause.

"I prayed for an opportunity to speak with you ever since I met you after the funeral," Vera told him. "God told me to witness to you."

Nicolai shrugged in weary disgust. He clearly thought Vera was crazy, and yet something about her words gripped him.

"Why do you think it is wrong for me to take money from the people?" he asked. "We have always done that."

Vera smiled. "It is not for me to correct your actions. You have to answer that question yourself from God's Word. God wanted me to ask you why you do it, but He is not telling me to explain it to you. I do know that if you ask Him honestly, He will tell you."

Her answer was so simple, so direct, and yet so profound that Nicolai did not know how to reply.

"I try to speak only what God tells me to say," Vera explained with a smile.

Nicolai extended his hand for the customary kiss he received at the end of every conversation. Vera hesitated only for a moment. Then, placing her work-worn hand in the soft hand of the priest, she shook it. "Just as if she were my equal," the priest later told his horrified wife.

"May God grant you to hear His voice," Vera said, and Nicolai felt as though he was the beneficiary instead of the benefactor this time.

That night Vera spent a long time in prayer for the priest. She sensed that the words God had given to her had indeed found an entrance in the skeptical man's heart. What Nicolai would do with the Word, she did not know, but she prayed that the seed would take root and bear fruit.

Unanswered Questions 19

The three sows lay in the sunshine, occasionally grunting when disturbed by a stretching neighbor. Once there was a general outcry of piggish complaining when, for some reason unknown to Vera, something upset all three. They trotted in confused circles, bumping into each other and squealing.

Before Vera could intervene with her stick, they all slumped back into their former companionable slumber. Vera settled herself once more on the stack of hay. "Lord, please keep those pigs where they're supposed to be," she breathed. "You know I could do little if they decided to run."

"They won't run," Larissa had assured her when Vera had posed just that question earlier. "They are too big and fat to do that. I think all three of them will have piglets soon."

"I really don't know if I can watch those pigs for you or not," Vera had told her neighbor doubtfully. "What can a little cripple like me do if they scatter?"

"Just for an hour or so," Larissa had begged. "I have to take my youngest daughter to school to register her for next year. I cannot find anyone else to watch the pigs for me."

So at last Vera had agreed to help her neighbor. She had ridden her bike out to the edge of the collective farm and propped it against the side of the huge dairy barn.

"Just sit here on the hay and keep them from ruining the hay pile," Larissa had told her. "I'll be back as soon as possible."

Vera burrowed herself into the haystack and pushed away irritating stalks from her neck. Her bent back found relief as she settled herself comfortably into the soft hay.

"Right over here." Vera jumped as a woman's voice sounded close beside her, just on the other side of the haystack. "Larissa is gone. I gave her permission to register her daughter at school."

Vera knew that voice. It belonged to Katya, the collective farm manager. A moment later two figures came into Vera's view, and she saw that Kolya, a middle-aged man of beefy proportions, accompanied Katya.

The man and woman stood gazing at the three sows. "Don't you think that middle one looks a little sick?" Katya smirked.

"Hmmm," Kolya responded with a knowing grin, "she does look a little under the weather."

Vera, concealed from the two speakers, sensed that something unusual was up and remained silent.

"That's the one," Katya said decisively. "We had better get rid of the one in the middle before she infects the other two. Do it right away." With that, Katya was gone.

Kolya stood still, looking at the sow he had been ordered to kill. "Probably has piglets inside," he muttered to himself. "Oh, well, have to do what the boss says." Taking a bottle from his pocket, he took a long swig, wiped his mouth, and replaced the cap.

"Okay, here we go," he said under his breath.

Vera silently watched the drama in front of her, knowing she would be powerless to stop the scheme. Kolya grabbed the sow in the middle, and when she began her death squeal as the knife slashed her throat, the other two pigs ran squealing around the side of the barn. Vera could tell that Kolya was an experienced butcher. In no time he had the pig slaughtered and was cutting her up with expertise.

Soon there were snarls and barking as the farm dogs, five mutts with voracious appetites and mean looks, came to investigate the sound of the dying hog. They circled Kolya, whining and begging with insistent growls of anticipation. "Get off," Kolya yelled more than once as they began circling closer and closer. The dogs slunk back and sat on eager haunches, their eyes gleaming red.

Kolya cut off a big slab of meat from the haunch of the butchered pig. Straightening, he looked cautiously around. Then he strode over to the haystack, and Vera could hear him pushing the meat into the haystack opposite her hiding place. He hurried back to the carcass just as the dogs closed in hungrily.

"Get out!" With screams of rage Kolya ran the dogs off. Looking back at the butchered pig, he bent over, and with one smooth stroke of his knife, he lifted a small unborn piglet by one hind leg. With a careless swing he tossed it across the fence into the adjoining field.

The dogs were after the piglet in an instant, and their savage growls as they fought among themselves came clearly to Vera's ears.

Soon the dogs were back. The one small piglet had only whetted their appetites. Several times they dashed toward the butchered sow, and every time Kolya shouted them back.

Vera held completely still and watched the scene in front of her. Finally Kolya had enough. Taking an armful of dead piglets—Vera counted at least eight—he called the dogs. Knowing what treat was in store for them, the mutts followed him eagerly around the corner of the barn.

Vera remembered the chunk of meat Kolya had carried to the hay pile. She scampered around the back of the haystack and found it buried in the hay. Almost without thinking she grabbed it, and even though it was heavy, she lugged it back around to her side and hid it completely under the hay. Then she returned to her vantage point once more. She quieted her breathing as she saw Kolya return, free of the dogs at last. He continued cutting up the pig.

Vera had plenty of time to piece together what was happening. Katya had been hungry for pork. She had enlisted Kolya to help her get the meat she wanted, and had probably promised him he would get his share for helping her deception.

Vera could imagine how the conversation had gone. Katya would have told Kolya that she had heard someone say that one of the sows had a contagious disease and needed to be culled.

Kolya would certainly have understood. There would have been an exchange of looks, with neither mentioning exactly what was going on, but both understanding what would happen. Sure, Katya would have known that to buy Kolya's silence, she would have to recompense him for his part in the theft of the collective farm's property. No doubt, as Kolya had butchered the sow, he had reasoned that Katya would not know if he privately "took" a big portion for himself.

Stealing and "taking" was all a part of the system that the communists had foisted onto the villagers. Everyone continually tried to pad their meager salaries with whatever they could take. From the lowest worker to the ones in authority, they all helped themselves as much as they could. No one spoke about it openly. Of course, there were many who were caught, severely reprimanded, fined, or even jailed. Ironically, the sentences were handed down and enforced by people doing the exact same thing. Building materials, grain for their own animals, garden tools, and whatever they could take—these were all considered fair game for the collective farm workers.

As Vera continued to watch, the dogs came back. Snarling among themselves, licking their bloody jowls, they again circled the butchering site, waiting for Kolya to finish so they could fight among themselves for the entrails. The piglets had been nothing more than an appetizer for the lean dogs.

Had the dogs not been consumed with the prospect of something more to eat, Vera felt sure that they would have discovered her. "Lord, shut their eyes to me," she prayed again. Vera was not sure just what would have happened if Kolya were to discover the silent witness to all that he was doing. It was obvious that he thought he was safe as long as Larissa was gone. Even then, he would tell her that he had been ordered to kill and dispose of the "sick" pig. That would explain all the blood and butchered mess beside the haystack. The dogs would presumably have done the rest.

Of course, he would have known that Larissa would not have been that blind to what really was going on. Perhaps he would even have "shared" some pork with her to keep her silent.

Nevertheless, Vera was pretty sure that Kolya would be highly upset if he knew that she had witnessed the scene from beginning to the end. Except for her quick shuffle to retrieve the piece of meat, she had hardly moved since the episode had begun.

"Lord, what made me do that?" Vera asked. "Should I have taken the meat?"

A moment later she saw Katya again. The manager had reappeared in her car, and the two conspirators swiftly put all the pork into the trunk. After a quick conversation, the woman left. Kolya allowed the dogs to attack the entrails before glancing over his shoulder and disappearing around the other side of the haystack.

Suddenly he reappeared, shouting obscenities and kicking furiously at the feeding dogs. The bewildered pack scattered as the man vented his anger at not finding his choice cut of meat.

"Thieving animals," he fumed as he stalked off.

"Here is the meat," Vera told her friend as she finished relating the story. "Was it wrong for me to take it? Should I return it to Kolya?"

Larissa snorted. "Was it wrong for Katya to kill the pregnant sow and take the meat for herself? Was it wrong for Kolya to agree to kill the 'sick' sow and take some pork for his pay?"

Vera listened sympathetically as her friend gave vent to her frustrations.

"Come on. We will take this home and butcher it ourselves." Larissa grabbed the hay-covered chunk of meat and stuffed it into her carry bag. Continuing her rant, she fumed, "Is it wrong for the government to rob the people of their land and forcefully consolidate it for themselves? Is it wrong for them to pay us so little that they force us to steal to feed and clothe our families? They know that everyone takes advantage of the system whenever possible. They themselves do it, and do they expect us to survive without resorting to the same measures? I have no idea what their concept of wrong is, but Vera, it was not wrong for you to take what was already ours. Don't they tell us that everything on the collective farm belongs to all of us? Is that not what communism is all about?"

The pork *was* delicious. Vera stretched out her portion as long as she could. Each time, she found herself pondering the complexities of living in a land where the government officials seemed to have little desire to do anything for the citizens except to feed them a steady diet of propaganda that did nothing to address their basic needs.

"God, I don't know what my place is in all of this," Vera confessed. "I wonder whether I should have done what I did. I am confused."

When she shared her thoughts with some of the sisters at church, it generated a lively discussion about honoring the government and obeying the letter of the laws or the intent of the laws. The unsettled questions remained.

"Lord, I will trust only in you to provide for me," Vera finally decided. "Just what is right and what is wrong about helping ourselves to the goods from the farm, I still do not know. But I would rather let you provide in your way than take anything that makes me doubt. I want to keep my heart open and my conscience free before you."

As usual, Vera found great comfort and solace in letting God take care of her unanswered questions. "I know there are many things you want me to understand and take by faith. But I cannot understand all things, for I am not you," she told the Lord sincerely. "Please reveal to me those things that you want me to know. The rest I will let you take care of."

The peace and contentment that crept into Vera's heart at this decision was far more satisfying than any of the pork she had eaten. "Better are my meals when I am confident of your presence, than any meal—no matter how fine and tasty—without you, Lord."

The Summons 20

"I have no idea where I am to go." Vera peered out the bus window and watched as a dizzying stream of traffic whizzed by in the streets of Vinnytsia. "This is a most unsettling thing for me."

The summons had been unsettling as well. At first Vera had tried to make sense of the official paper from the colonel of the Vinnytsia Communist Party. At last, with her characteristic acceptance of happenings she did not understand, she shrugged off the wondering why and bought a bus ticket for the two-hour trip to Vinnytsia. She had been summoned, so she came.

"Lord, help me find the right place," Vera prayed, trying to guess what the colonel's headquarters might look like. She had no memory of ever having been in this city before, and certainly not at any official address.

The woman on the seat beside her looked sharply at Vera and then drew away suspiciously as she heard the crippled woman praying under her breath.

"Please . . ." Vera began again. Then she laughed aloud as she saw a sign on the building beside her, announcing in bold letters that these were the offices of the colonel. "Oh, I must get off at the next stop," she called loudly as she got up.

When the bus deposited her at the next stop, Vera stood in the middle of the sidewalk and tried to find the office building again. Passersby brushed against the slight figure, and Vera stood to one side, scanning the cityscape. There it was, rising up importantly, all of three stories.

Grasping the handrail, Vera struggled up the twelve steps to the front door. Tall, barred windows frowned out onto the street, and the door was heavy. It took all of Vera's strength to open it.

Inside, a uniformed man was sitting behind a desk in the enormous hall. Doors along the two walls were tightly shut, and the ceiling soared up to the second floor. An enormous clay planter held twining vines that were almost devoid of leaves, and a slender tree with narrow leaves stretched upward about the height of a man. There were no other furnishings, although Vera saw the familiar photographs of the Russian premiers staring lifelessly down at her.

"Get out!" The man behind the desk frowned at Vera, motioning angrily with his hand for her to leave. "This is no place for beggars."

Vera ignored his attempt at intimidation. Walking calmly toward him, she pushed the paper forward. "You told me to come, and here I am." Another uniformed officer appeared from one of the side doors. "So, what do you want with me?" Vera asked. "You told me to come all the way to Vinnytsia, and here I am. It took me two hours, and the ticket was so expensive I don't even have money to get back."

The two officers read the paper together. The one sitting down looked curiously at Vera and told the other officer, "Take her to his office."

The standing officer hesitated and then turned. "Follow me," he said and marched briskly down the hall. When he realized he was not being followed closely, he glanced back and slowed his steps a little.

At the far end of the hall, he paused and pointed to a door. "That is his office," he said. Then he turned and walked briskly away.

Vera hardly paused before marching to the heavy door and giving it a strong push. The door opened swiftly and banged against the wall.

The well-dressed man sitting at his desk raised his eyebrows as the door opened and Vera's bent figure appeared in front of him. She looked curiously around his office. "Are you the colonel?" she asked without hesitation.

The official was intrigued by the abrupt intrusion and opened his mouth to ask just who she was. Before he could speak, Vera said, "I was sent this letter, I suppose from you, so here I am. Will this take a long time? I have traveled far, and I am already tired." Vera placed the summons on the desk.

Glancing at the letterhead, Colonel Stanislav got up and walked to the door and closed it. Vera heard the click of a lock.

"Have a seat," he said in a formal manner.

"Thank you, sir," Vera said gratefully. "At the village office, they sit and I have to stand, crippled though I am. God bless you for your kindness."

The colonel raised his eyebrows as Vera mentioned God, but he said nothing. Taking his seat once more, he read his own letter.

Opening a drawer in his desk, Stanislav drew out a brown envelope and removed a pack of photographs. One by one he wordlessly spread them out on his desk, facing Vera. She looked curiously at the men in the photographs.

Her glance lingered on one familiar face. Brother Masnetski looked up at her from the photograph. He was a traveling evangelist who had visited their church in Khmilnyk on several occasions. She remembered that he had officiated at funerals she had attended. Vera had often been blessed by the words of encouragement that the kindhearted brother spoke to the congregation.

Stanislav's shrewd eyes saw Vera's glance linger over Masnetski's photo. Reaching out, he pushed the photo toward Vera. "Do you know this man?" he inquired sternly.

"I don't know that man." Vera looked up at the colonel with clear, blue eyes.

Stanislav furrowed his eyebrows and looked sternly at Vera. "How is this?" he demanded. "This man has preached at your church many times, and yet you say you don't know him? I saw that you recognized him when you saw his picture. How is it that a believer lies to me?"

Vera's voice was firm and steady. "You asked me if I know him. We have a saying here in Ukraine that unless we have eaten with someone more than once, we do not know each other. I have not eaten with this man, so I told you the truth. If you had asked me whether I had ever seen this man, I would have said yes. I have seen him more than once.

Do not scold me for answering according to our tradition."

The words from the brethren came to Vera just then. "Do not say more than you are asked," they had cautioned Vera when they heard about the summons. "It is better to remain silent than to disclose any information, no matter how harmless it seems." At the memory of the warning, Vera covered her mouth with her hand. Had she said too much already?

A slight smile toyed at the corners of the colonel's mouth for a brief second. Then he glanced at the letter again. "Where did you go to school?" he asked.

Vera considered the question for a moment. It seemed innocent enough, so she answered carefully, "At our village in Filiopil. Only for three years, and then I had the accident that crippled my body." Reflectively she continued, "Actually, I was in the school of pain and suffering for ten years. I lay like a log day after day, hardly alive in my body but active enough in my brain. Yes, I am still going to school."

"Can you read?"

Placing her forefinger on the desktop, Vera said, "Yes, of course. I read your letter telling me I had to come here. I can read quite well."

Shuffling among his papers, Stanislav pulled out a scrap of paper. "Here we have a paper from an anonymous writer, stating that you hold illegal meetings for young people at your house."

Ah, so that was what this was all about! Religious gatherings at private houses were forbidden by the communists. This was what had sent pastors to prison, disrupted families, and deported people to Siberia. Would she face a prison term for inviting her friends from church and having services at her humble home?

"I have no family to suffer for what I do," Vera had told her church family. "So no matter what they do to this cripple, no one else will have to suffer. Let them hang me from the rafters if they will."

But now she said nothing to the colonel. She just sat in her chair, looking at him and waiting for his next move.

"Sign here." Stanislav abruptly shoved a paper toward her.

"What is it?" she asked. "There is too much writing on the paper."

"Just sign," was the terse reply.

"Sir, I will not sign anything without reading it. If I sign my name to a document, it means I am stating that this paper is true and I agree with the statements. God holds me accountable for anything I sign my name to."

"Then read it," Stanislav replied peevishly. "And there is no God, you know."

What he heard next was certainly not what he had anticipated from the stooped little woman. She shot up as straight as she could and burst out, "If there is no God, who took care of me all the time when I was a cripple? Who kept me from taking my own life when I was too discouraged to live? Who sent me fish to eat for nine months? Who has taken care of this cripple since my mother died? What power gave me the strength to lift my old uncle from his bed and help him go outside so he wouldn't soil the bed? Tell me who you think did all that, and then I will tell you it was God!"

"Your uncle must have been a mighty small man," Stanislav said testily.

"Oh, he was as tall as you are. He wasn't any too thin, either. I knew that it was better for me to help him than to have to change his bed, so even though it took an hour every day, that is exactly what I did. If God had not helped me, you can see there is no way in the world I could have done it. I tell you, God does exist."

The two faced each other across the desk.

"God is telling me something right now," Vera said simply. With a clear gaze, she looked straight at her interrogator. "You have a gun in here, don't you?"

The question startled Stanislav. He frowned darkly.

"You have a loaded pistol in your desk drawer," Vera told him confidently.

The statement caught the man off guard. "How, how . . ." he stammered.

"God tells me things," Vera said. "I hear from Him many times. For some reason He has chosen to talk to me, even though I am just a poor crippled woman."

After just a short pause, she repeated, "Your gun is loaded. When I came in here, you locked the door because you meant to do something evil. I felt the darkness that tried to overtake my spirit at that moment, but the Spirit of God inside me is stronger than any evil. This is the God whom I serve." Vera heard herself speak the words boldly and confidently. She knew that the Spirit was speaking through her, and that God was showing Himself strongly. She felt light and happy and free of fear.

The man in front of her nervously dropped his gaze and began toying with a piece of paper on the desk.

Vera continued to speak. "I know you think you have power over the believers. I know that you are trying to erase Christianity from our country. You will not succeed, for Jesus is more powerful than any of you imagine. The power of Christ in us is greater than the god you serve." Her words continued to flow at the man who had summoned her to his office.

"Enough!" With wild eyes Stanislav tried to stem the flow of words. Jerking a box from under the desk, he dumped Bibles and songbooks on the desk. "Do you have any of these in your house?" he demanded.

Standing up, Vera placed her hand on one of the Bibles. Ignoring his question, she admonished him, "This is what you should read. This is what has taught me about the God I am telling you about. If you read and ask God to show you the truth, you will never be the same again. He will change your life."

Stanislav stood up, his shoulders sagging slightly. He pointed to the door and said resignedly, "You may leave now. I have no more questions."

"Oh?" Vera, too, stood up. "Now I am to go? Just like that you throw me out?"

"Yes. I have no more questions. You are free to leave."

Shaking her head slightly, Vera exclaimed, "You send this paper to me and ask me to come here, spending money for a ticket, and now you think you can just send me back? How am I to buy a ticket to go back home? Could you live on sixteen rubles a month and still have money to take long bus trips?"

Digging into his pocket, Stanislav held up a ruble. "Here, take this. Believe me, this is all I have." Taking her by the elbow, he escorted Vera out the door.

As soon as the door closed behind her, Vera turned and opened the door again. "Sir," she told the startled Stanislav apologetically, "I forgot to thank you for the ruble. I want to thank you and wish you God's blessing. In that Book it says we are to be thankful for everything." She pointed to the stack of Bibles still on the desk.

"I don't have any more money," Stanislav pled. "I really did give you all that I have."

"No, you don't understand," Vera said. "I am not asking for more. I'm just thanking you and asking God to bless you for giving it to me, a poor crippled woman."

This time Stanislav escorted her outside more graciously. Then, backing into his office, he locked the door behind him.

Outside on the sidewalk Vera felt weariness flood over her. She looked for the bus stop but could not remember where it was. Sinking down on her knees on the sidewalk, she prayed, "Lord, how will I find my way home? I don't know where the bus station is, much less which bus to take home. Please help, Lord."

A gentle hand took her by the shoulder and lifted her to her feet.

"Brother Masnetski!" Vera gasped as she recognized the friendly face staring at her in surprise. "What are you doing here? I just saw your picture in that building!"

"Come, sister. Where do you need to go?" he asked kindly. "Maybe we should move away from this building."

The kindly evangelist helped Vera buy her ticket and find the right bus. All the while, Vera recounted her experience with the colonel. More than once Brother Masnetski murmured, "God bless you, sister," as the strange story unfolded. At the end of the saga he said, "Truly, Vera, you were led by the Spirit of God. May the seeds you have sown bring abundant fruit."

Even after Vera's bus had left, Masnetski found himself shaking his head again in amazement. "What faith!" he marveled. "What a testimony!"

"They Shall Bear Thee Up" 21

Vera pedaled down the highway, headed home after a church service in Khmilnyk. Spring was in the air, and freedom was in the air in Ukraine. Everywhere there was talk of the sudden liberty that was dawning with the collapse of the discredited Soviet communist system.

Vera had watched with grateful awe how the church sprang into action as soon as they were no longer fettered by the authoritarian rule of the communists. Evangelization began first in the city, followed soon after with small groups of people going into the villages and inviting people to church.

It was truly amazing how a change in government could mean so much for the believers. No longer were any of the pastors arrested for preaching in cities other than their hometowns. People could now freely meet in homes and churches for worship.

Vera slowed her bicycle and made a right turn toward home. The cobbles on the village street did not make for easy bicycle travel, so she rode alongside the road on the narrow path that cyclists used.

She was tired, but the trip to church was always worth the pain and effort it cost her, for her spirit was always refreshed by the experience. She usually sat in her corner in the back, worshipping in her heart and listening as the leaders ministered to the congregation. Today she had in her pocket a copy of a song she long had wanted. The tune had kept going through her memory, but there had been blanks between words.

Now at last she could fill in those blanks.

"You should sing in the choir," one of the women had told her. "You have a beautiful voice."

Vera had laughed. "A beautiful voice does not make a beautiful form. How would I look, all bent over and small, standing up front with the rest of the choir? No, I will stay in my seat, singing my songs to God."

Whenever someone asked her if she found it difficult to accept the limitations of her handicap, Vera's reply was made without bitterness: "Why should I keep thinking about what I can't do when there are so many things I can do? I do not have time or energy to think about all my limitations, for I am too busy praising God for what He has already done for me. My salvation in Jesus, the presence of God through His Spirit, the ability to take care of myself and my garden, and even being able to ride my bicycle to church are blessings so profound and wonderful to me that I cannot and will not complain about what I can't do."

Vera coasted down the slight slope that went past the pond, gaining speed to make it easier for her to pedal up the other side of the dip. Suddenly she felt something give way on her bike, and the front wheel wobbled crazily. "Lord Jesus, help me!" she cried as the bicycle skidded sideways onto the cobblestones and she was catapulted over the handlebars.

In the brief second when she was airborne, Vera cried out, "Lord, here I come!" The rounded tops of the stones rushed up to meet her wide-open eyes. Vera tensed for the impact.

Then, just as her outstretched hands touched the hard stones, Vera felt her body suddenly cradled by giant, invisible hands. Those huge hands held her slight form as easily as though she were an infant, and she had a distinct feeling of being cradled gently for a moment before she was softly lowered onto the road. Even her head came to rest as painlessly and gently on the cobble stones as if she had been eased onto a pillow.

"Thank you," Vera breathed. She lay still, her entire being suffused with a feeling of awe and gratitude. Wave after wave of euphoria swept through her as she realized what had just happened.

"Oh, God." Tears of joy squeezed out of the prone woman's eyes. "You have shown yourself full of mercy to me. 'Lest thou dash thy foot against a stone.' You love me so much that you caught me and laid me down gently."

A ripple of laughter escaped her as she continued to lie on the road. "God, you closed the lions' mouths for Daniel, saved the three Hebrew men from the fiery furnace, and gently placed me right on the cobblestones here in my own village," she chuckled to herself.

So still did she lie, basking in the glory of Jesus, that she did not realize anyone had seen her bicycle wreck until she heard the sound of running footsteps.

"Vera!" A man's worried voice called out to her. "Are you . . . are you dead?"

To this ludicrous question, she was tempted to reply, "Yes," but she said nothing. If she replied at all, the questioner would know she was alive.

She heard the booted feet move around her body and heard the quick intake of breath as the onlooker studied her prone position.

He obviously expected her to be seriously injured, if not dead, so Vera moaned a little, moving her arms slightly.

"Oh, she's alive!" Vanya's voice showed more consternation than before, and his steps circled her again, apparently at a complete loss to know what to do next.

Vera had mercy on her would-be helper and ended her little joke. "Do you want to help me?" she asked.

"What can I do?" Vanya asked helplessly.

"Just help me get back up."

"But surely you can't walk! I saw you wreck, and the way you went sailing through the air, it's a miracle you're not dead. Surely you can't walk."

Without even waiting for his help, Vera picked herself up and stood as straight as she could.

"This is amazing! You don't even appear to be hurt! There is no blood or anything," Vanya babbled, gaping at her.

"You mean you're disappointed?" Vera pretended to be offended. "Here I am, a weak cripple, tossed out on the road by that old bike, and you say there is no blood as though you had hoped there would be." Her eyes twinkled merrily.

Vanya wrinkled his brow. "No! No! I am just amazed that you can get up by yourself. Are you all right? You might have an internal injury you haven't even noticed yet."

"I have been a companion of pain for years," Vera told him. "If something hurts, trust me that I will know it. There is nothing wrong with my body that I don't know about. I have almost constant pain, but this time, nothing hurts. I was caught by some giant hands and lowered slowly to the road so I wouldn't be crippled even more," Vera finished as she went to look at the wreckage of her bicycle.

"But it's utterly impossible." Vanya was unable to believe what he was seeing. "Such a wreck at the speed you were going should have killed you."

"But it didn't kill me," Vera said calmly. "Like I said, God reached out and caught me and laid me down on the road as softly as though I were a baby. For some reason, He wants me to live on earth a while longer. I have not yet fulfilled the mission He gave me."

"Did you hit your head on the road?" Vanya asked suspiciously.

Vera laughed. "I don't have a concussion, if that's what you mean. Give your heart to Jesus, Vanya, and you might be able to understand me when I tell you how He took care of me in this wreck. He really does look after His people. Now could you be so kind as to drag this wrecked bicycle back to my house?"

"You must have been drunk," the other villagers told Vanya when he told them about the scene he had witnessed.

"No," he insisted. "I was following Vera on my way to the village. Just out there by the pond, I saw her bicycle skid sideways and fall, and she went flying over the handlebars onto the road.

"When I came to her, she was lying so still I thought she was probably dead, but suddenly she moved and sat up!" Vanya threw his hands into the air.

"I kept asking her if she was hurt, and she kept insisting that someone had caught her and laid her down. 'As gently as though I were a baby,' she kept saying. There was no blood, no broken bones, nothing wrong with her at all."

"The bike sure is wrecked," a neighbor man said. "I saw it in her yard."

Vanya nodded. "It was a terrible wreck. She should be dead or at least in the hospital, but she has not a single scratch. She just got up and walked away."

The story made a stir in the village, and when people questioned Vera, she would always tell them, "Yes, God caught me and put me down gently. I felt His hands as clearly as anything. Now try to tell me there is no God who takes care of His people."

Faith or Fear? 22

"She said she couldn't continue to stay at home. I tried to tell her we would manage somehow, but you know Natasha. She said she is twenty-five years old and will not be a burden to us. So off she went to Kiev to try to find work." Maria dabbed at her eyes and tried to stem another fresh flow of tears.

"Why did you not want her to go?" Vera asked her friend. "Is there no church in Kiev that will help to guide her?"

Maria nodded. "There is. She is going to my sister's house, and my brother-in-law is the pastor of a good church there. It is just that I wish Natasha could have stayed here. I worry so much about my daughter."

Vera pushed her bicycle slowly as the two women walked together. She and Maria left the churchyard and headed for the bus stop.

"I prayed with her before she boarded the train this morning," Maria continued. "That is all I could do."

"Seems to me that was the best thing you could do for her," Vera said with a smile. "I know of no better way to release someone than to send them off with a prayer of blessing."

Maria nodded. "I know." Then she added, "It's just that I have so many fears. What if Natasha gets swept into the wrong crowd, or some young man meets her and she doesn't know the dangers of this world?"

The bus stop was deserted. Vera leaned her bike against the side of the little building and sank down on the seat. Maria sat down beside her.

"Maria, dear sister," Vera said firmly yet kindly, "you are letting Satan influence your thinking. You are not putting your daughter and her future into God's hands. You have tried to keep her here. She did not stay. Is there anything you can do about it?"

Maria shook her head. "No, Natasha felt sure she was supposed to go."

"Then if she is out of your hands, you have to release her into the hands of God. As a mother, you can only do so much. Your concern for your daughter is good, and yet when something is taken out of your control, God wants you to release that to Him. That is why we call Him God. Because He can do what no one, not even a parent, can do," Vera said with conviction.

"This lesson is something God has been teaching me. I know there are things that are out of my control, and God wants me to let Him care for them. There are still times when I wonder how my needs will be taken care of, and I begin to worry. Then God reminds me of all the times He has cared for me. I am now almost sixty years old, and many times I wonder just how I am to survive as I age. But every time, I hear God telling me to trust in Him. So I am not just speaking to you, Maria. I am speaking to myself as well." Vera felt a stab of pain in her lower back and eased herself against the side of the building.

"I do want to be free of this fear," Maria said brokenly, "but I don't know how. Every time I try, I feel it coming back again."

Vera reached out and took her friend's hand. "Let's tell God all about it," she said, slipping to her knees. Maria quickly looked around and then joined Vera in kneeling on the asphalt. Vera prayed for the Spirit of God to replace all her friend's fears with trust in her loving Father.

So lovingly and simply did she pray that Maria felt peace restored to her heart and was comforted greatly. "God was right there at that bus stop," Maria told someone later.

The noise of the approaching bus drew the two women from their knees, and Maria embraced Vera fondly. "You are such a blessing to me," she said, bending to kiss Vera's cheek.

The bus lumbered off as Vera waved goodbye to her friend. Then she pulled herself up from the seat, and steadying herself against the side of the shed, she went to get her bike.

A great weariness engulfed her, and when she tried to raise her right leg to mount her bicycle, she could not lift it at all.

"Come on, leg," Vera pleaded, but it was as though her legs had turned into heavy weights that would not obey her mind. Her left leg was as heavy and wooden as her right one.

"God, now what?" she asked. "It's still a long way to home." The weariness in her legs wanted to spread over her entire body. "Is this where I will die and my spirit will return to you? Is this where my body will be found?"

No one was in sight. The bus had turned around at this final bus stop, for a bridge was being repaired farther down this road, and all traffic had been rerouted.

Vera checked the landscape. It was utterly deserted. She did not even see a shepherd boy watching sheep anywhere nearby. She was the only person there. "Yet, I am not alone," she told God. "I know you are here with me and will never leave me nor forsake me. Even if I die here, I know I will die in your presence."

Sinking down on the ground, Vera continued talking matter-of-factly to God. "Well, I have walked with you for almost forty years. They have been forty years of blessings from you, God. Without you I would still be lying helplessly in my bed. Maybe I would even have died long ago. I marvel at how you came to visit me through Uncle Viktor and helped me find Jesus. That miracle still moves me greatly, Lord. Of all the people in our village, even in our region, that you should hear the cry from my heart and send the Gospel to me! How great is your name, Lord!"

The sun began its slow descent toward the western horizon. Several times Vera tried to get up, but always her legs refused to cooperate. At times she dozed, only to be jerked awake again as her upper body slumped to one side.

No one came to the remote bus stop all afternoon. Vera wondered if the bus would make a scheduled stop in the evening.

"Lord, will you please send help?" Vera prayed. "I don't really want to spend all night out here, even though it is summer. I need help."

It was more than a mile back to Khmilnyk, but Vera finally tried to drag herself with her arms in that direction. Almost immediately she was forced to give up. "I can't!" she gasped. "The strength is just leaving me."

Her limbs quivered and she broke out in a sweat. "I think I have a fever," she said to herself. Her mouth felt parched. Was she going to die of thirst in this forsaken place?

"Lord, please help," she prayed again and again.

Late in the evening she heard the sound of an approaching vehicle. Twisting herself around, she cocked her head sideways to hear better.

Definitely, some kind of motor vehicle was coming. Vera dragged herself closer to the road, pulling herself forward with her hands, ignoring the stones that tore open her fingers.

"Help!" she yelled as a small car drew closer. She waved her right arm as high as she could above her head.

Mercifully, the driver saw her and stopped.

"Sister Vera!" The man who exited the car hurried over to her with concern. "What is happening? Why are you here beside the road?"

"Brother Leonid! Now the worms won't eat my body in this forsaken place." Vera felt relief sweep over her.

"Why do you say that?" Leonid asked, squatting down beside her.

"I thought I would die here," Vera told him bluntly. "All at once I lost the ability to move my legs, and no one was here to help me. Maria left on the bus before I realized I couldn't walk. I have been here all afternoon waiting for someone to come help me."

"God sent me," Leonid told her. "I was on my way home after preaching in Vinnytsia, and on the way I felt God put you on my heart. 'Go see Vera,' were the words I heard in my heart.

"At first I thought it was just my imagination," the pastor continued. "But the words kept coming to me over and over again until I turned the car and came here."

Vera smiled. "And God never told you that the bridge was out, did He?" Her mind was reeling at the wondrous deliverance God was bringing to her.

"Bridge out? What bridge?" Leonid asked quizzically.

Vera nodded her head. "That's what I figured. If you had known the bridge was out, you would have followed the detour to see me, and you would have missed me here. Yes, God told you to come see me because I needed to be rescued. He did not tell you to go the other way around the bridge, because then you would not have come by here. God is the most wonderful Father I can imagine."

Leonid nodded. "I am seeing that truly God moved in my heart to come seek you out," he said reverently. "He certainly heard your prayer for help." Then noticing Vera's bleeding knuckles, he said gently, "Let me help you to the car. I will take you home."

"My bike," Vera said. "It's still over there by the bus stop."

"I'll put it into the trunk once I have you inside." He picked up Vera with ease. "Are you getting enough to eat?" he asked with concern.

"I do not go hungry very often," Vera said simply. "God sends manna to me over and over."

"There," Leonid said, settling Vera into the passenger seat of his car. "Now let's get that bike."

Vera sighed. "God, I thank you for hearing me. Forgive me for doubting you and allowing fear to creep into my heart." Remembering her earlier conversation with Maria, she laughed at herself.

"I was praying and asking God to remove Maria's fear," she told Leonid as he turned around to take the other road to Vera's house. "Now I need to ask God to replace the fear in my own heart with trust and acceptance of His providence."

The kindly pastor helped Vera into her house and put the bicycle inside the yard. "Are you sure you are all right?" he asked with concern. "Who will look after you if you need help?"

"God will," Vera said simply and trustingly. "I have so few answers to the questions that come, but I do have the greatest answer of all, which is God. I am learning that there really is no other answer. Thank you, dear brother, for allowing God to use you to help this old crippled woman today. Now you need to go to your family, or they will wonder what has happened to you. Tell them about the goodness of God to a poor old woman who needed rescuing." Vera smiled at her benefactor and waved off his concerns. "I will be all right. God will take care of me," she said with conviction.

"Patient in Tribulation" 23

"Good morning, Jesus." Vera opened her eyes to see the summer sun bathing the early outdoors. Several months had passed since she had lost the use of her legs. She lay on her side, facing the window, and immediately began her morning talk with God.

Hers was not an elaborate, ritualistic prayer, but one of deep worship. She calmed her mind and heart before God, allowing the Holy Spirit to prompt her prayers. Perhaps her morning prayers were more worshipful in nature than her nighttime prayers. When she woke up in the night, usually because of discomfort or pain, Vera had learned to always ask the Lord the same question: "God, whom do you want me to pray for right now?"

Her testimony was simple. "I know if God leads me to pray for specific needs or people, that prayer is often the method He uses to help me forget my own discomforts and troubles. I find it soothing to lay the cares of other people before God and allow Him to direct me how to pray."

On this morning Vera sat up in bed like usual. Using her hands, she lifted both useless legs off her cot and slid to the floor where she knelt to pray. Even though the position was not comfortable, Vera felt a deep desire to kneel during her morning prayers. Placing her hands together, she prayed out loud as she began thanking God for His presence and provision.

Her rooster began to crow right outside her window. He clucked importantly among the hens as they scratched for any early food they could find.

Vera grabbed the side of her bed and straightened her upper body. She pulled the sheet up and tried to make the bed. "No use being slovenly," she told herself as she smoothed the coverlet with a work-worn hand. "Every woman likes to have her home tidy."

That task completed, she began her slow journey across the floor, sliding backward on her knees, propelling herself with her clenched fists.

It had taken days of agonizing movements to find the best method of locomotion after Vera lost the use of her legs. At first she had tried pulling herself along on the floor with her hands. Although her body weight was very slight, she had quickly exhausted her strength as she had tried to drag herself about the house. It was only after many tries that she had finally found the least strenuous way of moving around: sliding backward on her knees, which she did by leaning forward and supporting her torso on her arms as she pushed with her closed fists on the floor.

When her knuckles had begun to bleed, Vera used her open hands to propel herself, but as soon as the bleeding stopped, she went back to using her fists. Eventually, after months of such treatment, her knuckles became calloused and hard and no longer bled.

Wearing thick pants under her skirt helped to protect her kneecaps somewhat from the continual friction of the wooden floor, but at first even that was not enough. Vera had to wrap cloth around her knees to keep them from bleeding. Finally they too became calloused enough to make the journeys less painful.

"Chickens first," Vera said, heading outdoors. In the entryway she stopped her awkward backward slide long enough to dip out a portion of the cracked corn she carefully hoarded to keep her chickens laying.

"Chuck, chuck," she called, and the little flock of five hens and one rooster came fluttering from around the back of the house.

Next Vera made her painful way on all fours across the yard to the outhouse. The dust in the yard was soon ground into her clothes, and her hands were covered with dirt.

Once back in her house, Vera poured a little of the precious water from a plastic bottle onto a washcloth and cleaned her hands. Then she pushed herself into her kitchen.

Resting for a moment, she tried to plan her moves carefully. The saucepan was at eyelevel, right under the workbench. The water was on top of her table, and the *kasha* was stored in a jar on a shelf underneath.

Pulling herself upright on her knees with strong and practiced arms, Vera poured water into the pan, set the pan on top of her small gas stove, and lit the fire ring with a match. Having accomplished that, she sagged wearily back to the floor to wait. When she finally heard the water boiling, she poured the *kasha* into the water. At intervals thereafter, she struggled to her knees again to stir the hot mixture.

The plain, cooked cereal was nourishing, if not especially tasty. At times she enjoyed a little sweetener when someone gave her a gift of honey, or on rare occasions when she indulged herself and sprinkled a little sugar on top.

"Enough left for lunch too," she said, peering into the pot. There were many days when Vera cooked a little extra in the morning and then ate the leftovers later that day. It was a bit monotonous, to be sure, but it did offer some relief from the arduous task of cooking.

"Good morning." It was Mikhail, bringing her daily bucket of water.

"Ah, God bless you, Mikhail," Vera said gratefully to the elderly man. "Somehow, you will someday receive blessings for helping an old crippled woman. Thank you for the water."

Mikhail merely grunted and nodded before turning to leave.

Just what had prompted her neighbor to take on the task of bringing her water from the village well, Vera never knew. Reserved and unsmiling, the elderly man had silently showed up after Vera could no longer walk, taken her pail, and fetched a daily bucket of water from the well. Naturally, one small pail was hardly sufficient, but Vera was not one to complain about small mercies received.

"Lord, I ask you to bless Mikhail with an understanding of your love," Vera prayed daily. "Soften his heart, and bless him for his kindness by revealing yourself to him."

The water Vera used to wash her plate was saved and poured into a bucket. This was water that her flock of chickens could drink later. Of course, they would also appreciate any stray kernels of *kasha* that remained from washing the dishes.

Her early morning efforts had tired Vera, but there was no time for rest. The rows of vegetables in the garden needed to be weeded and thinned, so she began her slow progress out the door, down over the stoop, and through the back yard into the garden.

Vera spent long hours tending to her vegetables. The planting and sowing of seeds took her three times longer since she could not walk. Her shortened hoe worked the soil a little awkwardly at first, and her spade seemed to have a mind of its own as she tried to dig from a kneeling position. Gradually she had forced herself to adapt, and actually became quite proficient at her garden work.

The neighbors helped sometimes, but Vera knew they had their own work, so she tried to do as much as she could by herself.

"Lord, your strength is most appreciated," she said out loud as she surveyed the long rows of work. "I pray for a good, strong day without downtime." There were days when she simply could not work for the pain. Sometimes she collapsed on the ground until the excruciating pain eased somewhat, while at other times she had to give up working in the garden for the rest of the day.

Larissa came striding through the yard gate. "Hello! Vera?"

"I am in the garden," Vera called in response to her friend's voice.

"As always," Larissa said, walking through the back yard. "You work harder in your garden than anyone else I know."

"What else do I have to do?" Vera quipped. "I cannot go work in the fields like you do, so I spend my days in the garden taking care of my vegetables."

"Look at you," Larissa mused aloud. "Holes in the knees of your pants, hands all dirty from pushing yourself on the ground, and yet there you are, smiling at me as though your life was as good as . . ." her voice trailed off, trying to find a good comparison.

"As good as any princess," Vera laughed. "In fact, I *am* a princess living in a castle. My Father is the richest King ever, and I am His child."

"Well, your majesty, I brought your groceries," Larissa said with a shrug. She had heard Vera's testimony many times.

"You may get the money from my bag. You know the place," Vera said. "Will you sit for a while and have tea with me?"

Larissa hesitated. "I don't know. I have so many things to do at home. But, well, maybe."

Vera nodded and began pushing herself toward the house. "You know where my things are," she said cheerfully. "Go ahead and make the tea, and we will sit outside on the bench. I need to get out of this sun for a bit anyway."

Larissa did indeed know her way around Vera's little kitchen. She put the teakettle on the stove and had the tea ready by the time she heard Vera outside.

The wooden bench was right outside the door next to Vera's chair, which had all four legs cut short for her convenience. Vera pulled herself up onto the chair and positioned her useless legs with her hands. She pulled her skirt down and looked at her hands.

"Not much use washing them," she decided, dusting them on the sides of her skirt. "They will just get dirty again, and I should save the water for better uses."

"You are the absolute limit," Larissa said, sitting down on the bench and placing Vera's teacup beside her. "You talk about being a princess, and yet here you sit, covered in dirt, and lacking even the water to wash yourself when you need to. When did you last have a bath, may I ask?"

Vera threw her head back and laughed at the idea. "Bath? Oh, my, Larissa, I don't know. I just use my washcloth early in the morning, and that has to be sufficient. Why, it would take buckets of water to bathe properly."

Shaking her head, Larissa took a sip of her tea. She made a wry face. "Don't you have any sugar?" she asked.

"Did you check in the jar behind the pickles? I think there was some in there."

Larissa went to the kitchen and returned with the small glass jar. "There's not enough. You didn't ask me to get sugar from the market," she chided.

"It's all right," Vera smiled. "I'm used to drinking my tea without sugar. You take the rest of it."

"Not enough money again," Larissa surmised. "Vera, I don't know how you do it on your small pension."

Before Larissa could say anything more, Vera held up her hand. "No, Larissa, don't go there. I am learning to be thankful to God for every small gift as well as the large ones. There is no room in my heart for complaining. If I begin to be the least bit unthankful, such a flood of self-pity would sweep over me that the goodness of the Lord would be pushed out. Daily I thank God for His gifts."

"I don't understand at all," Larissa said, draining her cup and rising to her feet. "Now you stay there and rest awhile. You look like you need it." Shooing away an inquisitive hen with a wave of her hand, Larissa placed the cups on the table and left.

Vera went inside, ate the rest of the *kasha* from breakfast, and then went back outside. On the way to the garden she checked the hens' nesting box. "Only two eggs," she scolded her pets. "Which of you isn't laying? Do you know what happens to hens that don't lay? They become stew pot chickens."

Vera knew the chickens would not actually find themselves in her cooking pots. She would send them to the market in hopes of raising a little more money. Soon she would need to figure out how to buy some more clothes. Scooting around on the ground wore out her clothes faster than she liked. "Lord, give me wisdom," she prayed as once more she went out to the garden to continue her weeding.

This day was like so many others since Vera's setback, and yet she was blessed by the comforting presence of the Holy Spirit. Her voice rose in songs of sincere praise to God as she worked. If she felt that the song did not adequately express her worship and thankfulness, she poured her heart out in her own words.

That evening the laborious journey back to her house was interspersed with several rest stops. She collected the two eggs, placed them in her apron, and carefully transported them to the house. She was hungry, but far too exhausted to cook, so she sliced bread from the loaf and chewed on it. Washing herself as well as she could, the tired woman felt almost too weak to continue. She was appalled at how dirty the water was. Oh, well, she would just use it all to wash with tonight and let the Lord provide for the next day. Perhaps Mikhail would bring her two buckets of water. Occasionally he did that.

On her knees beside the bed, Vera once more quieted herself before the Lord and began her worship. She felt peace restored to her heart as the Comforter soothed her weary heart and body. As she clambered up onto her bed and tried to find a comfortable position, Vera thrust away the pain that engulfed her. Over and over she repeated the words, "I will bless the Lord at all times. His praise shall continually be in my mouth."

The darkness of the summer night washed over the village, and the lights in the houses went out one by one. Stars twinkled overhead. The nighttime insects sang their own music. At last asleep, Vera lay in a fetal position, her work-worn right hand stretched out to one side as though clutching an invisible hand for support.

Hindering Help 24

"Sasha, do you need to go to the outhouse?" The shrill tones of the elderly woman's voice were jarring in the silent night.

As the loud voice broke into Vera's sleep, she awoke instantly and sighed, "Oh, Lord, surely not again!" She turned to her other side and tried to burrow her head under her thin pillow.

"What did you say?" The man's question was equally strident.

"Do you need to go to the outhouse? I have to go."

"Wha-a-a-t?"

The old lady's voice rose in pitch, "Do you have to go to the out-house?" she fairly shouted.

"No!" bellowed her husband, matching her volume.

"Come anyway," she demanded. "You will have to go later, and you might as well go now."

In spite of the pillow covering her head, Vera could plainly hear the dialogue between the elderly couple.

"What?" Sasha's voice rang out in the dark house once more.

Evgenia's reply came again, louder than ever.

Every night Vera woke up to the now-familiar shouting match from the couple who had come to live with her.

"It will be wonderful for you," several of the women from church had assured her when the idea was proposed. "They can help you with your household chores and give you companionship for your long days and lonely nights. What a wonderful plan!"

"God, I should have asked you more specifically before I allowed them to come live with me," Vera now said into the darkness. "How long is this madness going to continue?"

The scraping and bumping in her room as the two finally got up, lit a candle, and made their slow journey outdoors, seemed to take a long time to Vera. She heard the familiar squeal of the front door hinges as they finally made their way outside.

Vera sighed. Sleep was out of the question for at least an hour. As difficult as it had been for her to get adequate rest before, it was now almost impossible because of the elderly couple's nightly drama.

This time Vera was so tired that she dozed while they were gone.

The door hinges squealed in protest again and Vera jerked awake. For a brief moment she could not figure out what was happening. Then it all came back with dismaying clarity as, with a bang that shook the little house, the two came back into the sleeping room.

Vera heard the usual bumps and loud sighs as the couple returned to their beds. Very quickly, loud snores indicated that at least two of the three occupants of the room were able to sleep.

Vera continued her conversation with God now that she was thoroughly awake. "Lord, it really did seem like a good idea to have Evgenia and Sasha move in with me. I thought they could help with the cooking and gardening. Sasha even seemed capable of doing things like . . . fixing the squeaky door hinge when they first came. It didn't work out that way, did it?" She moved restlessly on her bed as her thoughts went to the first weeks after the old couple had moved in.

"Oh, we have to have sour cream with our borsch," Evgenia had informed her hostess. "Sasha will not eat it any other way." The money to buy the luxury had come from Vera's pension. The demands continued to build as the old couple loudly informed Vera of what they "had" to have.

"I have more than twice the work I used to," she now complained. "I know I am to give thanks in all things, but this seems too much. Teach me what to be thankful for, Jesus."

Not only did the new occupants make continual demands for groceries, they also seemed oblivious to anything they could have done to lighten the burden. For most of the day they either sat out in the yard talking loudly to each other, or they took long naps indoors. Very seldom did either of them do anything to help with the household chores.

"I don't think this plan is going to work," Vera finally told her pastor's wife.

Ludmilla studied the face of the woman whom she had learned to love like a family member. "Why not?" she inquired sympathetically.

"They are too old to work," Vera explained. "They add a great deal of work for me. Now I understand why their son and daughter-in-law were so eager to find a new place for them." Vera told her friend about the nightly episodes.

"We had no idea," Ludmilla told her, trying to hold back her smile at Vera's vivid word picture. "We thought it would be beneficial to all of you."

"That's what I thought," Vera nodded. "But you see, they do even less now than when they first arrived. Their age is really beginning to show."

"Does the extra money help you at all?" Ludmilla questioned.

Vera said nothing for a moment. Finally she replied bluntly, "There is no extra money. I buy all our groceries from my own pension."

"That cannot be permitted!" Ludmilla exclaimed. "They both get a pension too. I know it is not very much, but neither is yours. Surely they knew they were to share the expenses of the household, especially for food!"

Vera pinched her lips together and just shook her head briefly.

"I will see if Pavel can come to visit you," Ludmilla said, pressing Vera's hand understandingly with her own warm one. "Let's pray right now about this situation."

"Thank you, Brother Pavel, for fixing that squeaking hinge," Vera told her pastor gratefully. "There are many things I can no longer fix, and now at least there is one less thing to annoy me."

"Sister, you are welcome. Now, if it is all right with you, I will just rest here on the sofa for the night. I must get up early tomorrow to catch the first bus back to Khmilnyk."

Vera lifted her hands. "Yes, you are welcome, but such a poor sofa! I wish I had a better bed for you," she lamented.

"No, no," Pavel said quickly. "This couch is fine. I can sleep almost anywhere."

Vera had felt honored when her pastor arrived before dark and ate supper with them. She had noticed how he had been observing her household as they ate. She did not mention anything to him about their situation until the elderly couple had gone to bed.

"Do you have any advice to give me?" she asked in her usual direct manner as they sat in the kitchen.

Pavel rubbed his hands together thoughtfully. "You know that when you agreed to take them in, it was considered a permanent arrangement by everyone. They needed a place to stay, and you lived here by yourself with enough room for them."

Vera nodded.

"I don't know of any solution except to advise them that you will not be responsible for their food any longer. It seems to me that Evgenia could cook for the two of them, even though she is elderly. I think she can actually get around better than you can. You will just have to be frank with her," Pavel told Vera. "Their daughter-in-law told us plainly that they would not take them back in."

"And I know why," Vera said wearily.

"When their old house was sold, everyone thought enough money would be left over to buy an apartment for their son and his family, plus enough for the elderly couple to live on. I don't know where all that money went." Pavel wrinkled his brow, puzzled.

Vera did not tell the pastor that she had a hunch about who had that money. It was mere speculation and would not help solve her current dilemma.

That night she spent a long time asking God what He wanted her to do. "If this is what I get for impulsively taking them in, or if you want me to learn something through it all, I want to be willing. I have never yet found a situation that you cannot redeem, Lord, although this one is too big for me to even imagine a good solution. Just help me to trust in you and continue to find fullness of joy in your presence. I can go through anything then."

"Do you have to go to the outhouse?"

The loud question woke Vera with terrible familiarity. Even though it scarcely helped, she tried to cover her ears and drown out the cacophony of sound that pierced the darkness during the couple's long nocturnal journey.

"What in the world is going on?"

Vera sat up. She had forgotten that Pavel was in the next room, sleeping on the sofa. "It's okay," she told him. "They are just helping each other go to the outhouse."

When the candle was lit, Vera could see her pastor watching the lengthy and noisy charade with furrowed brows. When Sasha and Evgenia finally exited, Pavel asked in a weary voice, "So this happens every night?"

"Yes, every night," Vera replied wearily.

Eventually the rickety pair made their slow yet noisy return journey back to their beds.

"I don't know how, God, but please free me from this prison I have made for myself," Vera prayed as the sleepless minutes ticked on that night. "Please, God."

"Before you go, I want you to count all your money," Vera told Evgenia and Sasha.

"What?" Evgenia cupped her hand behind her ear. She looked intently at Vera's bent-over figure.

Vera tried to speak directly to the old woman. Raising her voice, she continued, "Count your money! I don't want any accusations that I stole any of your money while you were here!"

Evgenia drew back and looked sharply at Vera. "Money? What money?" she inquired innocently.

Vera sighed. Evgenia might be hard of hearing, but her mind was still plenty sharp. "All the money you brought with you when you moved in a year and half ago. I want you to count it and make sure it is all there."

Evgenia reluctantly drew out her purse. Turning her back to Vera, she began counting out stacks of money.

"It's all here," the old woman said after she had put the bills back in her purse.

"I hope that all will go well with you at your daughter's house," Vera said loudly. "I pray that you may find God and trust in Jesus for your salvation."

"What?" Evgenia cupped her hand behind her ear again.

"May the peace of Jesus be with you," Vera shouted.

Evgenia nodded and turned to leave. Sasha was already in the yard, standing beside their few packed suitcases and waiting for the promised ride. Vera watched through the window as the elderly couple climbed into the car that drew up outside her yard. Then the car bounced off into the distance, and her house was silent.

"Blissful silence," Vera said exultantly. "God, I thank you for answering my prayer by providing a place for my guests to live. I tried to accept my lot, but I think I failed many times. I'm afraid I did not show your love to them very well. My crippled legs did not give me an excuse to be impatient, but truly, I cannot help but be thankful that you did answer my prayers and I can have my house to myself again. Even though I thought I would enjoy having someone around, why would I need anyone when I have you?"

The tired woman sat and rested, basking in the silence. That night, her house remained quiet and restful.

The Wheelchair 25

"This is pitiful," Nikita said, looking at Vera, who was pushing herself through the dirt in the garden.

"What is?" Vera asked, looking up from her position beside the cabbages.

"That you have to be down in your garden like this. It's pathetic. You're not able to walk, not able to get around decently in your own yard, and you're always filthy from crawling through dirt."

Vera's response was a huge grin and her usual answer. "I don't feel sorry for myself, so why should you? I am the treasured princess of the King! His castle is my house and He lives here with me."

"Pshaw!" The young man kicked at a dirt clod. "I don't know what you're talking about."

"I am talking about Jesus," Vera said bluntly. "He is the King!"

"I don't see very much of Him caring for your needs," Nikita said scornfully. "Some princess you are, wallowing around in the dirt like an animal."

"Son," Vera said tenderly, "you see only the outward circumstances. You see me groveling in the dirt, and you do not see my joyful spirit. Inside this crippled body, pain-wracked and weary, lives the very presence of my Jesus in the form of the Holy Spirit. He is with me always. He helps me get from place to place so I can take care of the garden, feed the chickens, and gather the eggs. He provides strength from hour to hour. In the night, when I can't lie down to sleep because of the pain in my body, He comes and ministers comfort to me that is beyond words. Nikki," she continued affectionately, "I feel that I can lean my head against the chest of Jesus. It seems I can feel Him touch me and love me. That is why I am a princess in spite of my circumstances. I would not trade my position in Christ with anyone else in the world."

"You know what?" Nikita said, turning away from Vera. "I remember seeing an old wheelchair in my neighbor's shed. I am going to see if I can get it for you."

Vera watched him run out of her yard. "Lord, I feel that you are touching him. Please save him."

"Here." Nikita was back in thirty minutes. "I had to promise my neighbor that I would hoe his potatoes before he would give me the wheelchair. It is torn a little here on the arm, but I can soon fix that."

Vera looked at the simple chair on wheels. "Thank you, Jesus!" she exclaimed. "I hope I can turn those wheels over this ground. Let me see."

She scooted herself over to the wheelchair and grabbed both armrests with her strong hands.

"No, no," she shook her head as the young man moved to help her. "If I cannot get on and off without help, this will be of no value. Remember, I live by myself."

It took tremendous grit and determination for the woman to haul herself up into the chair, but she finally did it. With a triumphant smile she turned to the kindhearted neighbor boy. "Look, the princess even has a throne!" she rejoiced.

She grabbed both wheels and pushed. The chair moved forward a little, but her useless legs dragged in the dirt, acting as a brake.

"Okay," Vera said, undeterred. "I see I have to go backward so my feet don't get stuck."

The progress from her garden to her house was bumpy and slow. Time and again she had to stop and rest. At last Nikita took the handles and tipped the chair backward, lifting her dragging feet from the ground. "I will help you whether you want me to or not," he said firmly. "You can do it by yourself the next time."

He easily wheeled her over the hard-packed dirt in her yard and stopped beneath the apple tree just outside her front door.

"Thank you so much," Vera sighed. "You are very strong. I will have to learn how to drive this thing backward."

"You need one with foot rests," Nikita said. "Then your feet won't drag, and you can go forward and see where you're going."

"I am the daughter of the King, and when He wants me to have one, I will get one," Vera reminded him.

Nikita left abruptly, unable to understand the language of royalty from the poverty-stricken cripple.

"Sister Vera!"

"In here!" Vera's voice came through the open door.

Pastor Vladimir walked inside, lugging a large item in his arms. "See what I brought for you," he greeted Vera. Unfolding a wheelchair, he placed it on the floor in her living room.

Vera crawled out of the kitchen. When she saw her new pastor and what he had brought her, she threw her head back and laughed in sheer delight. "Oh, Lord, you are so good. Another wheelchair! And this one even has footrests so I can go forward."

Vladimir was puzzled. "Another one? You already have one?" He looked inquiringly around the small house.

"Yes. My neighbor boy brought me one just recently. Without footrests," she said soberly, looking up at her pastor. "This one is better, but I really don't need two. Maybe we should give this newer one to someone else."

"I know of no one else who needs even one," Vladimir assured her.

Vera hauled herself up onto the chair. Lifting each helpless leg with her hands, she positioned them on the footrests. Eagerly she grabbed the wheels and pushed forward. "Ah, how smoothly it rolls on the floor," she exulted. She spun the wheelchair around in a tight circle, marveling at its lightness.

"This will be so much better," her pastor told her. "Now you can go from room to room and get around without crawling on the floor."

Vera smiled up at him and simply replied, "If you would like some *kompot* to drink, please help yourself. It is on the table."

"Thank you," Vladimir said as he stepped into the kitchen. "Do you want me to bring you a cup?"

"Yes, please," Vera replied, still propelling her chair in small circles.

"We will thank God for this wonderful gift," Vera said when he returned. "Will you pray with me?" The two bowed their heads. Vera felt the presence of God in the humble room as her pastor prayed God's blessing on her house and on her life. When it was her turn, Vera thanked God for the wheelchair. "Thank you for the better one," she said simply.

"I am such a blessed woman," Vera told her pastor gratefully after they had finished praying. "I live by myself, but I have a large family—my church family."

Vladimir made a mental note to ask his wife to bring some of the sisters one day to help clean Vera's house. Even a man could recognize that this house needed help.

After her pastor left, Vera rolled herself to the doorway. Yes, just as she had guessed, the wheelchair was too wide to go from room to room as Vladimir had suggested. This would be an outside chair.

"At least I can now go forward," Vera said to herself with genuine gratitude. She plopped herself onto the floor, her useless legs softening the fall. She struggled to return the chair into its folded position.

It took her ten minutes to get the chair and herself out of the house. By then she was too tired to open the chair again, so she sat on the stoop of her house, resting her head against the outside wall.

"Jesus, I am a princess. I am a princess because you are a King." Over and over she repeated these words. Two of her inquisitive hens came over to check if she might have some tidbits. Vera's eyes closed and her body slumped wearily against the house.

Provision 26

"Vera!"

All was quiet in Vera's yard. The hens scratched hungrily around the front door, and a cat meowed in plaintive tones, arching its back and rubbing against Larissa's legs.

"Vera! Where are you?" Larissa called.

All was silent.

Larissa pushed open the front door and went into her friend's house. "Vera?" she called out again.

The inside of the house was cool and silent.

"Oh, God," Larissa crossed herself apprehensively and went into the kitchen.

A cooking pot was on the stovetop, the *kasha* inside shriveled and congealed into a solid mass. A spoon lay on the floor.

Larissa hurried into the room where Vera usually slept. The blanket on the cot covered a form so shriveled, so small, that once again Larissa crossed herself and hesitated before she braved crossing the short distance from the door to the cot.

"Vera." Larissa stretched her hand out reluctantly and touched the bony shoulder that protruded from a corner of the blanket.

A weak moan was all that Vera could manage. But at the response, Larissa sighed and said, "Oh, thank God. You are alive."

"Water," was Vera's feeble, whispered plea.

Larissa bustled to the kitchen and returned with a glass of water. She held Vera's head up and tipped the glass slightly so the thirsty woman could drink. "You are all wet," she exclaimed as she pulled the blanket back. "Oh, my! You have a terrible fever too."

"Call Deacon Yuri," Vera managed to say with great effort. "Please, call Yuri."

<hr/>

"I am sixty-five years old," Vera told the small group of friends gathered in her house. "I have no relatives to inherit my house, and I don't want the government to take it. In exchange for some help from them, I will leave the house to Pasha and Sveta if they agree to bury me when I die—like I almost did last week. If Larissa had not come and found me, I think I should have died from thirst. I could not move from my bed, and no one heard my calls for help."

Olga, the young pastor's wife, reached out and took Vera's work-worn hand in her own. Tears pooled in her eyes as she rubbed the sick woman's hand gently. "That must have been a terrible experience for you," she said compassionately.

Vera nodded and continued, "So the Lord has showed me that I need help. After my experience with Sasha and Evgenia, I told the Lord I didn't want any more help. I thought I would never want anyone to live in my house with me. Now I see that I need someone to look after me. Even my wheelchair doesn't help me if I am too weak to drag myself onto it." She glanced at her wheelchair in the corner and said thankfully, "Although that chair has been a tremendous blessing to me, I realize I still need more help than it can provide."

Times were hard in Ukraine since the economic downturn occurred after the few prosperous years the country had enjoyed in the nineties. Suddenly real estate prices fell, and the government no longer issued loans for people to buy property.

"We tried to buy the house across the road, but we were not given a loan," Sveta told the group. "We really need a place for a garden since Pasha lost his job at the construction site and my salary does not pay enough for us to buy groceries."

"I have a big garden," Vera said. "I don't need all that space to grow my own vegetables. If you would be willing to help me, you could grow all you need for your family. You have four children, do you not?"

Pasha nodded and his wife answered, "Yes. Sasha is married, and Vanya lives in Kiev. Nadia works in the government office, and Katya is still in school. We have fallen on very difficult times." She wiped her eyes on her sleeves.

"I asked God about having you stay with me, and I believe it is His will," Vera said simply. "You need to ask God also for an answer in your own hearts."

"We will pray," said Yuri, the deacon from the church in Khmilnyk. The visitors stood and bowed their heads.

"Lord, we seek your direction," Yuri prayed simply. "This is not a light undertaking, but we believe you are leading Vera in making this decision. We want only your will." The others all prayed in turn. They quieted their hearts and listened for direction and leading from God.

"This is more than just making it legal with the village office and getting the council to acknowledge Vera's signature," Yuri told the group after they took their seats again. "This is also a binding agreement before God. It is not a light undertaking for you, Brother Pasha and Sister Sveta. Traveling from Khmilnyk out here regularly will take from your time and the limited funds you have. Does your car still run?"

Pasha nodded. "It does most of the time," he chuckled. The decrepit car was over twenty years old, and most of the time it seemed to run more from sheer desperate need than from mechanical power.

"Many times when we make business agreements, we need to spell out the details of such an agreement," Yuri continued. "This is a spiritual agreement as well as a business agreement. Do you have any suggestions, Vera, concerning what you want Pasha and Sveta to help you with?" Yuri asked.

Vera shook her head. "I don't want anyone to be bound by details," she said firmly. "I want to accept such help as I need and let God direct all of us. It is not for me to say what should be done. I trust God to work in all of us and to direct us." After a pause she added, "I know the other time it did not seem to work, but I am willing to try again. I cannot deny that I need the help."

Sveta said quickly, "Oh, sister, we truly want to help. I know we can work together, and I see your needs. I want to help you with much more than just the garden. I can help you with the needs in the house and with your laundry."

"You sisters will work well together," Olga said with a smile. "I know Sveta well enough to know that she will not let Vera's needs go unattended."

"Then we will make an appointment to take you to the village office and get this notarized and made legal," Yuri said. "I am so blessed to see how God is putting this all together. Sister," he concluded as he turned to Vera, "are you satisfied?"

Vera turned her eyes up to look confidently into her deacon's gaze. "I'm much more than satisfied. And why not? The King always looks after His princess." Her easy laughter filled the room.

Sveta removed the clothespin from the towel and pulled the last of the laundry from the line. She deftly folded the towel and put it on top of the basket.

Pasha and Katya were at work in the garden. The rows of potatoes were neatly weeded and everything was growing luxuriantly. Generous rainfall was promising an abundant harvest.

"There," Sveta said to Vera, who was shelling a bowlful of peas outside on her chair, "that should take care of the laundry for the week."

"Oh, God bless you, sister," Vera said gratefully. "I am still ashamed of how reluctantly I accepted your help at first. God is showing me how much I need to learn to accept help even though it is hard for me to become dependent on other people."

"For many years you managed to take care of yourself, even though you are handicapped. I still often marvel at how you managed," Sveta said kindly.

"It was the King," Vera chuckled. "He never let me give up."

"I know that no one will ever know how much you have suffered in your life," Sveta continued. "Even since we started coming out here once a week, my eyes have been opened to many things you have endured that none of us even imagined before."

"You also probably don't know how often the Lord came to me and carried me away in the Spirit while I was going through those times," Vera said, her voice growing soft with the memories. "Oh, I am a blessed princess, the daughter of the King."

Sveta said nothing, but a feeling of awe swept over her again as she felt the impact of the older woman's faith and testimony. "We are the ones who are blessed," she said softly, almost to herself.

"Look, God has blessed our garden so abundantly," Vera exclaimed, running her hands through the peas. "For a long time we were never even able to plant peas. Then the Christians in America gave us the seed packets, and now we eat peas! Oh, Sveta, we are rich! We are rich children of God!"

"I need to be reminded of that," Sveta said. "Just today while we were coming out here, our car began sputtering again, and I began complaining about our loss of income and about how difficult our lives have become."

"I am learning that true contentment is not found in things of this earth, but by resting in the will of God," Vera said. "So many times I have fretted because I did not know how God was going to provide—even though He provided so many times for me—and found my faith had run low. So I gather my manna from Him every day, and I find He is good."

The yellow cat arched his back against Vera's legs and meowed softly. Vera picked up a short stick and used it to push open the door to the entry-way. The cat strolled inside and settled itself on a shelf inside the window.

"Well, you have some extra water from the rain two days ago," Sveta said, appearing at the front door with two pails. "This will help fill the water barrel."

"See!" Vera chortled. "Even a leaky roof brings a blessing."

Sveta shook her head at such reasoning. "I will have to find another bucket for the new leak. Quite a puddle had formed in the corner of the kitchen. I will have to ask Pasha if he can tar that roof again."

Both of their thoughts went to the problems of trying to keep Vera's old house weatherproof. The roof was the major problem right now. How long would those fragile asbestos sheets hold up? And how could they ever afford to put on a new roof? The most thankful attitude still did not prevent the rain from pouring in through the leaks.

"'The Lord is my shepherd; I shall not want.' I take it that means I will be taken care of. When I die, I will live in a mansion without a leaking roof," Vera said with her usual bright smile. "I choose to think about that. How long I still have to live here is God's choice, but I know I will not die until my work here on earth is finished. I do wonder sometimes what that work is which He expects me to do."

"I don't wonder," Sveta said to herself as she poured the water into the barrel. "I know exactly how He is using her to minister to the hearts of His children."

The Present 27

"Hello, Vera! It is Nadia!" The girl's clear young voice floated through the open door of Vera's house.

"Oh, bless the Lord!" Vera called from her sitting position on the cot. "You have come again!"

A fresh breeze accompanied the young woman as she entered Vera's house. "See!" she said cheerfully. "I picked a bouquet of flowers from the roadside after the bus dropped me off. I will find a jar and put those flowers right beside you so you can smell them and admire their beauty."

After the flower arrangement was made, Nadia asked, "Now, have you eaten today? I will make you some *kasha* or anything else you would like. How about an egg, nicely fried and with a piece of bread? Or is there something else you would especially like?"

Vera held up her right hand and looked at the girl fondly. "Nadiyka," she said, using the affectionate form of the girl's name, "whatever you make for me is fine. Yesterday I never even had to cook once, for the food you made on Monday was still very good. Here you are again, ready to cook for me once more. What has happened to my life? How is it possible that God is blessing me so much by sending you to me three times a week, and your parents also come almost every week to look after me. I . . . I . . ." Vera's voice trailed off and tears of joy filled her eyes. "I am so blessed. I am highly favored by God. You are so good to me."

Nadia smiled. "Truly it is the hand of God," she said simply. "He has made the way for you to receive these blessings through His children."

Vera looked around the room. "Look how wonderful everything is! Everywhere I look, there is only order and cleanliness. The windows sparkle, the curtains are washed, and the floor is clean. Oh, Nadia, at night when I draw the blanket up under my chin, I enjoy the fresh smell of the clean blanket and thank God for you. You wash and clean and cook, all for me! I am a princess! I truly live like a princess!"

Nadia laughed. "Hardly anyone else would say that you live like a princess. This small house and the life you live as a cripple—most people would not think that a sign of being favored of God."

Vera shook her head. "Oh, but my young friend, it is not just my clean, orderly house that makes me feel like a princess. It is because I know my Father is the King that I am always aware of my wonderful position in Him."

It was easy for Vera to block out her earthly surroundings and live in a heavenly kingdom, for she constantly lived in a state of gratefulness and praise to her Lord. More than once Nadia had noticed that the elderly woman easily transitioned from the earthly to the heavenly in her conversations. Nadia nodded her head without saying anything.

"You know, Nadia, for many years after I could no longer walk, I felt so alone and helpless in this world. Sure, I had my brothers and sisters in the church, yet during the week I had no one I could really fellowship with about Jesus. Plus, I would try to keep myself and the house clean, and I just had to give up because I simply could not do it. All I could do was prepare meager meals and do the most basic, necessary things around here. Now look, all that has changed."

Nadia nodded again. "I am sure it was not easy for you to try to look after yourself," she said. "I don't see how you could even do it."

"It was never easy to push away my longing for a clean bed, for clean clothes, and above all, for a proper way to bathe. When your father made that outside shower in the back yard, I felt so unspeakably thankful. The first time I used it, I just could not get finished letting the water run over me in streams. To be clean again was so wonderful! Clean outside as well as inside!"

Nadia was in the kitchen now, starting breakfast preparations. She opened the small refrigerator door and got out an egg. Quickly she lit the gas stove and placed the frying pan on top of it.

"It is a wonder that God's people care so much for each other," Vera continued. "Look how you do all this for me."

"You know I am not the only one." Nadia wouldn't take all the credit. "There are many others who are providing the means for all this to happen."

"Yes, I am completely overshadowed by God's presence and cared for in such a marvelous way through His children. Only a few months ago I was trying to manage by myself during the week, waiting for your parents to come out here on Saturdays to help me. Now I have you to help every other day. Thank you," she finished gratefully.

The smell of the frying egg reached her. "Now I even get to eat some of the eggs from my own chickens," Vera marveled. "I don't have to save and scrimp all the time just to buy the necessary things I need. My needs are met by the blessing of loving people."

When Nadia brought her plate in to her, Vera pulled the young girl down beside her on the cot and began to pray. "Dear God, my heart is overflowing with praise for you! How is it possible that I, a crippled woman, am so highly favored? I praise you, Lord, and I thank you. I thank you for all the people who have heard about my condition and have generously helped me. You know I have tried never to complain to anyone, yet your children have so lovingly shared gifts with me so that I can have this wonderful life.

"God, I don't even know how to thank you, except to say that once more I give my heart, my life, my tongue, and this crippled body to you. I am yours."

Vera's Bible—the love letter from her King.

Vera's bedroom—the place of many conversations with her Father.

Afterword

At the time of this writing, Vera continues to live alone in her house, receiving regular help from Nadia and her parents. Her house is now cleaned, her clothes washed, and her food prepared, even for the days when she is by herself.

"I have need of nothing. God is providing everything for me. I am so blessed," Vera declared adamantly. She still scoots from room to room, for the doorways in her house are too narrow to accommodate her wheelchair. She still sleeps in an upright position because it is too painful for her to lie down. "God tells me to pray for people when I am awake at night. From now on I will also pray for you," she told us during our visit.

Even though generous donors have made her life much easier since Nadia comes in to help care for her, Vera still lives a very primitive life. In spite of her poverty, she does not ask for anything for herself. In fact, when Christian Aid Ministries staff visited Vera and told her they wanted to help Ukraine's poor and needy, she suggested they look elsewhere since her Father was already meeting her needs.

All her hardships pale in the light of her bright smile, her cheerful manner, her easy laughter, and above all, her faith in Christ. It is in this that her true character is revealed, as she recounts the times of knowing that God has been with her during all her difficulties and hardships. No bitterness or anger seems to surface as she freely talks about her life. Her conversation is constantly laced with references to her King and about herself as the princess.

When my wife and I left her for the last time, Vera prayed in her usual simple manner, "Lord, I thank you for bringing these people to my house. Thank you that they want to help your people who are in need. Help them to find the poor and needy. Bless them for their compassion and love. I know that even in America there are many who love you and are true believers. Now let them go in the peace of God. Thank you that I became a relative to these people. How would we ever become family if it was not for you, Jesus? Thank you that you took care of them as they traveled. I pray to you, my God, to help me in my life. You know my struggles here. I also pray for the brothers who are preaching your Word everywhere. Please take care of them. Amen."

That prayer created a holy place and time. We all felt the presence of God, and we count it a tremendous privilege to have met Vera, the King's Daughter.

—Harvey Yoder
February 2010

Glossary

sala	SAH lah	*raw pork fat*
Sasha	SAH shah	*familiar term for Alexander*
Stanislav	stah nee SLAHV	
Sveta	SVYEH tah	
Vanya	VAH nyah	*John*
vareniki	vah REH nee kee	*boiled dumplings filled with potatoes, sauerkraut, cheese, or fruit*
Vasily	vah SEE lee	
Vinnytsia	VEE neet syah	*a city in west central Ukraine*
Vladimir	vlah DEE meer	
Volodya	voh LOH dyah	
Yuri	YOO ree	

About the Author

Harvey Yoder and his wife Karen live in the beautiful mountains of western North Carolina. They have five children, all of whom are married, and eight grandchildren. A teacher for many years, Harvey is now a licensed real estate agent in addition to being a prolific writer. He has traveled extensively while gathering materials for his many books, most of which have been published by Christian Aid Ministries. Harvey finds it especially fulfilling to write the inspiring accounts of faithful believers whose stories would otherwise remain unknown. His greatest desire in writing is that his readers will not merely be entertained by the stories, but rather be motivated to seek God with all their hearts.

Harvey enjoys hearing from readers and can be contacted by e-mail at harveYoder@juno.com or written in care of Christian Aid Ministries, P.O. Box 360, Berlin, Ohio, 44610.

Christian Aid Ministries

Christian Aid Ministries was founded in 1981 as a nonprofit, tax-exempt 501(c)(3) organization. Its primary purpose is to provide a trustworthy and efficient channel for Amish, Mennonite, and other conservative Anabaptist groups and individuals to minister to physical and spiritual needs around the world. This is in response to the command ". . . do good unto all men, especially unto them who are of the household of faith" (Gal. 6:10).

Each year, CAM supporters provide approximately 15 million pounds of food, clothing, medicines, seeds, Bibles, Bible story books, and other Christian literature for needy people. Most of the aid goes to orphans and Christian families. Supporters' funds also help clean up and rebuild for natural disaster victims, put up Gospel billboards in the U.S., support several church-planting efforts, operate two medical clinics, and provide resources for needy families to make their own living. CAM's main purposes for providing aid are to help and encourage God's people and bring the Gospel to a lost and dying world.

CAM has staff, warehouse, and distribution networks in Romania, Moldova, Ukraine, Haiti, Nicaragua, Liberia, and Israel. Aside from management, supervisory personnel, and bookkeeping operations, volunteers do most of the work at CAM locations. Each year, volunteers at our warehouses, field bases, DRS projects, and other locations donate over 200,000 hours of work.

CAM's ultimate purpose is to glorify God and help enlarge His kingdom. ". . . whatsoever ye do, do all to the glory of God" (I Cor. 10:31).

Additional Books

PUBLISHED BY CHRISTIAN AID MINISTRIES

God Knows My Size! / *by Harvey Yoder*
How God answered Silvia Tarniceriu's specific prayer
251 pages $10.99

They Would Not Be Silent / *by Harvey Yoder*
Testimonies of persecuted Christians in Eastern Europe
231 pages $10.99

They Would Not Be Moved / *by Harvey Yoder*
More testimonies of Christians who stood strong under communism
208 pages $10.99

Elena—Strengthened Through Trials / *by Harvey Yoder*
A young Romanian girl strengthened through hardships
240 pages $10.99

Where Little Ones Cry / *by Harvey Yoder*
The sad trails of abandoned children in Liberia during civil war
168 pages plus 16-page picture section $10.99

Wang Ping's Sacrifice / *by Harvey Yoder*
Vividly portrays the house church in China
191 pages $10.99

A Small Price to Pay / *by Harvey Yoder*
Mikhail Khorev's story of suffering under communism
247 pages $10.99

Tsunami!—*from a few that survived* / *by Harvey Yoder*
Survivors tell their stories, some with sorrow and heartbreak, others with joy and hope.
168 pages $11.99

Tears of the Rain / *by Ruth Ann Stelfox*
Poignantly honest account of a missionary family in war-torn Liberia
479 pages $13.99

A Greater Call / *by Harvey Yoder*
What will it cost Wei to spread the Gospel in China?
195 pages $11.99

Angels in the Night / *by Pablo Yoder*
The Pablo Yoder family's experiences in Waslala, Nicaragua
   356 pages $12.99

The Happening / *by Harvey Yoder*
Nickel Mines school shooting—healing and forgiveness
   173 pages $11.99

In Search of Home / *by Harvey Yoder*
The true story of a Muslim family's miraculous conversion
   240 pages $11.99

HeartBridge / *by Johnny Miller*
Joys and sorrows at the Nathaniel Christian Orphanage
   272 pages $12.99

A Heart to Belong / *by Johnny Miller*
A Heart to Belong (sequel to HeartBridge) continues the story of God's
sustaining grace as the Millers love and guide the children of the Nathaniel
Christian Orphanage in Romania.
   302 pages $12.99

The Long Road Home / *by Pablo Yoder*
Will prayers and the Spirit's promptings bring young Pablo "home"?
   456 pages $12.99

Miss Nancy / *by Harvey Yoder*
The fascinating story of God's work through the life of an Amish
missionary in Belize
   273 pages $11.99

Into Their Hands / *by Harvey Yoder*
Bible smugglers find ingenious ways to transport Bibles into Romania and
the former Soviet Union.
   194 pages $11.99

A Life Redeemed / *by Harvey Yoder*
The inspiring story of Ludlow Walker's journey from his childhood in
Jamaica to his current calling as a minister of the Gospel. An unforgettable
story of God's redeeming grace and transforming power.
   232 pages $11.99

The Way to God and Peace

We live in a world contaminated by sin. Sin is anything that goes against God's holy standards. When we do not follow the guidelines that God our Creator gave us, we are guilty of sin. Sin separates us from God, the source of life.

Since the time when the first man and woman, Adam and Eve, sinned in the Garden of Eden, sin has been universal. The Bible says that we all have "sinned and come short of the glory of God" (Romans 3:23). It also says that the natural consequence for that sin is eternal death, or punishment in an eternal hell: "Then when lust hath conceived, it bringeth forth sin: and sin, when it is finished, bringeth forth death" (James 1:15).

But we do not have to suffer eternal death in hell. God provided forgiveness for our sins through the death of His only Son, Jesus Christ. Because Jesus was perfect and without sin, He could die in our place. "For God so loved the world that he gave his only begotten Son, that whosoever believeth in him should not perish, but have everlasting life" (John 3:16).

A sacrifice is something given to benefit someone else. It costs the giver greatly. Jesus was God's sacrifice. Jesus' death takes away the penalty of sin for everyone who accepts this sacrifice and truly repents of their sins. To repent of sins means to be truly sorry for and turn away from the things we have done that have violated God's standards. (Acts 2:38; 3:19).

Jesus died, but He did not remain dead. After three days, God's Spirit miraculously raised Him to life again. God's Spirit does something similar in us. When we receive Jesus as our sacrifice and repent of our sins, our hearts are changed. We become spiritually alive! We develop new desires and attitudes (2 Corinthians 5:17). We begin to make choices that please God (1 John 3:9). If we do fail and commit sins, we can ask God for forgiveness. "If we confess our sins, he is faithful and just to forgive us our sins, and to cleanse us from all unrighteousness" (1 John 1:9).

Once our hearts have been changed, we want to continue growing spiritually. We will be happy to let Jesus be the Master of our lives and will want to become more like Him. To do this, we must meditate on God's Word and commune with God in prayer. We will testify to others of this change by being baptized and sharing the good news of God's victory over sin and death. Fellowship with a faithful group of believers will strengthen our walk with God (1 John 1:7).